Reclaiming Our Bodies

Healing Exercises
for Survivors of Childhood Sexual Abuse

Rebecca L. Zuckweiler, M.S., R.N.

with

James M. Zuckweiler, M.A.

Parkside Publishing Corporation
205 West Touhy Avenue
Park Ridge, Illinois 60068

Reclaiming Our Bodies

ISBN 0-942421-45-0

Printed in the United States of America

10 9 8 7 6 5 4 3 2

Library of Congress Catalog Care Number: 92-64458

With unconditional love and a feeling of gratitude that we have been blessed with the experience of sharing life with them, we dedicate this book to Carly, our precious daughter, and to Ruth, our treasured mom.

Contents

Acknowledgments

With respect and appreciation, I want to thank Jean R. Eckerly, M.D., for reviewing portions of this book for its medical accuracy and for her open-mindedness that allowed me to be properly diagnosed and treated. I also want to acknowledge Pamela A. Morford, M.D., Elliot Francke, M.D., and Alan L. Arvidson, D.C., for their medical competency and kindness as they helped my body to heal.

I want to extend a heartfelt thanks to Michael J. Maley, Ph.D., L.C.P., who so professionally and compassionately guided me through five years of psychotherapy.

My most exciting moment throughout the entire process of writing this book came when I received that first friendly and encouraging telephone call from Terry Spohn, Executive Editor at Parkside Publishing Corporation. He has helped me complete a book that matches my original dream.

My dear friends Dede and Sharon deserve a great deal of credit for showing me I am worthy and lovable, and for encouraging and supporting me throughout the process of writing this book.

Last but not least, I want to acknowledge Jim, my best friend, husband, and partner in parenting our beautiful daughter. This book could not have been written without his emotional support, countless hours of work, and incredible writing skills.

Preface

I have worked as a psychotherapist treating victims of sexual abuse for many years. During this time, I have repeatedly been asked by clients to provide answers to questions that reflect certain basic themes. What is incest? How could he do it? Why did he pick me? Is it normal to feel this way? Am I taking too long to get over this and am I simply feeling sorry for myself? Why am I ill all the time? How do I go about feeling better? Will I ever be free of the damage inflicted upon me during my past? It is the purpose of this book to share some answers to these and other questions that arise within the context of sexual abuse.

A colleague of mine once told me that she believes knowledge leads to power and, as a consequence of this belief, she endeavors to provide clients with information so that they might exercise their personal power and accept responsibility for their own change. My motivation for writing this book stems from the frustration I have experienced as a direct result of not having a relatively simple book to hand to clients when they express: (1) their need to understand what happened to them as sexually abused children; and (2) their desire to comprehend what they might expect to experience as they struggle to recover from the trauma of sexual abuse.

I have observed and guided many women and men through the recovery process associated with incest and other types of childhood sexual abuse. It is my belief that what is most needed in terms of navigating through this complex and often frightening journey is a book that speaks from a practical and experienced level to which victims of sexual abuse can relate. Consequently, this book is not a scholarly composite of research findings; rather, it is a sharing of personal and professional knowledge designed to help incest victims come to grips with and eventually shed their role as victims. It is also a guide to experiencing the joy connected with learning to take charge of one's own life.

I am typically a very private person who very selectively discloses the personal details of my life. I have made a decision to extend my boundary of privacy because I believe that doing so will be helpful to others who are at various stages within the abuse recovery process. In addition to the information I have gained as a result of treating clients, I have learned a great deal from my own painful yet ultimately freeing process of recovering from the effects of incest. It is my hope that this book will lessen the struggle for other victims of sexual abuse through my offering both clinical and personal observations illustrating how people can reach the light at the end of what can be a dark depressing tunnel.

The clients to whom I refer in this book are actual people who have been treated by me. I do not present any names because of my concern for confidentiality. Similarly, the privacy rights of members of my family of origin are protected due to the fact that I have a different last name.

Introduction

Incest scars its victims many ways. The most significant damage results from an unconscious splitting of mind, emotion, and body, thereby causing us to lead detached, fragmented lives. This splitting serves as a defense mechanism that shields us from the full impact of our thoughts and feelings during a time of great vulnerability, but it also leads us to abandon important parts of ourselves and to lose our sense of integration. It causes us to abandon our bodies, which store memories and hold emotions. Splitting from our bodies cuts us off from painful but potentially healing memories. It also blocks us from experiencing and ultimately integrating powerful feelings of fear, sadness, and anger. Our bodies were taken from us and then used, abused, and finally tossed aside. It's time we reclaim them.

One of my clients, a woman in her mid-thirties who has struggled for years to comprehend and overcome her childhood incest victimization, reflects the depth and extent of her personal recovery when she writes, "It's been a year now. A year ago, during the 4th of July celebration, I was in a hospital. I sat looking out the wire-reinforced window at the fireworks, watching others celebrate.

"[I knew] if I could feel better about myself and change myself, that things around me could be more positive as well. I was able to get angry, I was able to cry and now I was able to forgive myself.

"It's the 4th of July again, and I am out there in the crowd, celebrating the meaning of this holiday, standing outside in awe as the sky is colored by the paintbrush of fireworks. It's good to be alive."

An Abuse of Power

Incest occurs whenever someone serving in a

protector role behaves in a sexual manner toward a younger person to satisfy the protector's sexual and emotional needs. Power exists in a relationship whenever one party is dependent upon the other party to get particular needs met. When a protector abuses power by sexually exploiting the needs of someone who is dependent upon him or her, incest is occurring.

People who serve in protector roles for those younger than themselves include parents, older siblings, grandparents, great-grandparents, aunts, uncles, cousins, babysitters, friends' parents, teachers, ministers, coaches, scout leaders, and others. Although incest is most commonly perpetrated by fathers and older brothers, it can be committed by anyone serving in a protector role.

There are at least two situations in which the protector isn't necessarily older than the victim, but the same abuse of power can occur. The first involves a relationship between a client and a psychotherapist or doctor. Adult clients are typically in therapy to deal with traumatic wounds inflicted during childhood, and this often requires that the therapist function temporarily as an agent for reparenting. The second case exists when an abuser is in a caregiving position with regard to an adult who is mentally or physically disabled.

The behaviors of incest are the same as those associated with adult sexual contact. Stroking and fondling of genitals and breasts, kissing on the lips when done to generate sexual feelings, and undressing of the perpetrator or victim for the purpose of sexual arousal are all examples of such behaviors. Incest includes oral, vaginal, and anal intercourse. It involves the infliction of pain on the perpetrator or victim when done for the purpose of sexual stimulation.

Incest Perpetrators

Understanding more about the types of people who commit incest is helpful for two reasons. First, seeing the similarity between a personality profile of a typical abuser and the personality of our perpetrator helps us break through the denial we may have regarding our childhood abuse. Second, this information allows us to understand why certain current relationships feel so abusive, and it aids us in avoiding relationships with such people in the future.

People do not commit incest because they are depressed, anxious, or alcoholic. These conditions are often contributing factors, but they are not the primary cause. People who sexually abuse their children are personality-disordered. This is a clinical term used to diagnose people whose personality traits are so chronically rigid and extreme that they experience significant blockage or interference in their ability to relate to others in healthy, socially appropriate ways. Most incest perpetrators suffer from schizoid, narcissistic, or psychopathic personality disorders.

Schizoid Personality Disorder

People with this diagnosis are emotionally aloof and expressionless, indifferent to others, socially retarded, and extreme loners who are incapable of establishing relationships with more than one or two others including family members. They were most likely raised in an environment of severe emotional neglect in which there was little if any opportunity to bond with others, and consequently they experienced limited chances to learn about appropriate methods for satisfying needs.

As adults, schizoids have minimal ability to differentiate sex from intimacy, and their relationships with spouses are typically distant ones. They are at high risk to exploit the needs of their children in an effort to satisfy both their unfulfilled childhood needs and current adult needs. Schizoids turn to their children because they lack the social skills to obtain gratification through healthy adult relationships, and because they have the power to control the children.

Narcissistic Personality Disorder

Narcissists are totally self-absorbed with an ego that won't quit. They possess an unlimited sense of entitlement, are very manipulative, and have little ability to empathize with others. They are split away from their emotions and consequently operate entirely through the head in an insatiable drive to possess power. In contrast to schizoids, they are socially active in their effort to attract attention, admiration, and validation from others.

Male narcissists typically have a history of being emotionally abused during childhood by rageful, power-hungry, and demanding fathers whom they could never please. They also often have seductive mothers who made them feel unique for the ways in which they satisfied their mothers' emotional needs. Emotionally deprived mothers, who had sex and nurturance confused, requested nurturance from them in ways that left them feeling very special, overly stimulated, and sexually frustrated.

As adults, male narcissists seek to prove that Mom was right about their uniqueness and that Dad was wrong about their worth. They do this by using their perception of power and feelings of rage acquired from interactions with their fathers to sexually and emotionally dominate females regardless of the female's age. The intense sexual charge within narcissists' bodies in conjunction with their confusion regarding sex and nurturance lead them to exploit females in an effort to satisfy their own needs.

Psychopathic Personality Disorder

Psychopaths, also referred to as sociopaths or anti-social personality disorders, are essentially narcissists without a conscience. They are amoral, have no regard for societal rules, and possess no capacity to differentiate right from wrong. Their actions are influenced only by their assessment of the risk of being caught. The thrill-seeking behavior so characteristic of psychopaths represents an unconscious attempt to compensate for being cut off from their feelings.

Psychopaths were most likely raised in a dysfunctional fashion similar to that of narcissists, only more so. They were shaped with little or nothing in the way of positive role modeling involving morals, rules, and principles. One or both of their parents may well have had a psychopathic personality disorder.

As rageful adults without a conscience, psychopaths often engage in particularly horrendous types of abuse. They are quite capable of violently raping their children. Sadism, child pornography, and child prostitution are frequently incorporated into the incest behavior of psychopaths if they believe they can get away with it.

1

Emotional Damage

When we begin to face the damage inflicted by incest, we might find ourselves feeling overwhelmed at how extensive it can be. One of the frequent consequences of being sexually abused is a lingering sense that life is a constant struggle against overpowering forces. Once we have learned to recognize that this feeling originates from our childhood and that we have the power to move beyond it, we begin to exert control and influence over our adult lives.

Obviously, the damage from incest varies from person to person. One incest survivor may relate to only a few issues presented here, while another will be amazed by how much of this material fits. Factors such as the extent of pathology within the family system, along with the frequency, duration, and type of incest experienced, determine the amount of damage sustained. The following checklist will help you identify some of the ways in which incest may have affected you mentally and emotionally. Ask yourself if any of these statements describe your actions or feelings.

- Life seems very hard.
- I feel down in the dumps most of the time.
- My sleep, appetite, energy level, and/or concentration are not what they should be.
- I think about suicide a lot.
- I use drugs or alcohol or both to help me cope.
- I am bothered by flashbacks involving my childhood.
- I cannot remember very much of my childhood.
- I often feel spacey and unaware.
- I often feel nervous, tense, or ill at ease.
- I feel panicky, my heart races, and I am dizzy, nauseated and sweaty—sometimes without knowing why.
- I eat compulsively, binge and vomit, or starve myself.

- I feel like I never had a chance to be a kid.
- I believe I am an unworthy, undeserving, and defective person who can never do anything right.
- I feel as if I am a sexual failure, but I use sex as a way to get nurturing and intimacy in relationships.
- I have self-mutilated or hurt my own body.
- I would be quite content never to have sex again.
- I am confused about my sexual preference.
- I have always had trouble learning and retaining information, and I feel stupid.
- I have difficulty trusting and getting close to others.
- Many of my relationships are one-sided, and I am always the giver.
- For males only: Projecting a macho image is important to me.
- For males only: I feel rage and I rarely, if ever, cry.

There is no universal approach to healing from incest, but survivors typically face many common issues in recovery. Remember, you are not alone and you are not crazy. Mending the splits inflicted by sexual abuse is difficult, but it is possible. This book will not delve deeply into every issue, but it will present some of the most typical emotional obstacles you will face as you begin your recovery.

Denial

Denial is a mental split from reality, and plays an enormous part in the life of an incest victim. It can take many forms, but I often see two major variations. In the first type, we mentally split off from the reality of what happened to protect ourselves from the devastating information. For example, we may deny any incest in our past to a psychotherapist we have gone to see about chronic depression.

This denial is a defense mechanism that lets us cushion ourselves from the cruelty of what happened until we are able to safely deal with it. This split can be seen as a wonderful subconscious method of taking care of ourselves. During childhood it may be very important to completely repress what happened, to convince ourselves it was no big deal, or explain it away as being no different from the experience of other children.

In the second type of denial, we split off from our own truth and take in the messages of others. One example would be an incest victim telling her mother about the abuse and being told she is making up a terrible story. The victim consequently comes to believe the incest did not occur. Accepting another's denial is rarely helpful. Generally it is something we encounter when trying to confront the incest. The perpetrator might engage in emotional abuse by suggesting that "everyone does it." Statements like this help feed denial. The abuser may simply lie and say he or she never touched you, or minimize the frequency or significance of it. A mother who has her own reasons to deny the truth might discount her daughter's report of incest by suggesting the daughter has an active imagination, is disobedient, or is trying to get her father into trouble to get even for something else.

Denial can be particularly troublesome when we are struggling to understand the memory fragments so common to early stages of recovery.

When we first start to see glimpses of our incest history, we often wonder if we are making it up. Learning self-trust is essential to mending the mental split from reality.

If you want to know whether you are lying to yourself when incest memories begin to surface, all you have to do is ask yourself. If you lied or imagined the incest, you'll know it. Denial is a subconscious defense mechanism intended to protect you from harm; lying is a conscious and deliberate act. Trust that you can look to yourself for the truth when incest memories begin to surface.

All too often, incest survivors seek validation of the abuse from the perpetrator. This is one of the greatest roadblocks to recovery, since abusers seldom admit their actions. They, too, often create severe splits to cope with the past. Permitting your recovery to be dependent upon the perpetrator is a setup to go nowhere. Remember, your recovery is not dependent on a confession from anyone. Regardless of what anyone else says, you can look into yourself with trust and know that you will let go of your denial when you are ready to face the facts, the pain, and the changes that go along with the truth. You will feel an inner drive to begin integrating your fragmented self. One critical ingredient is being in a safe place so you can handle the impact of the information. It's not uncommon for people to be in their thirties, financially stable, and even have children of their own before their subconscious decides it's safe enough to break through the denial.

Letting Out the Secret

A common way of broaching the subject is to tell your spouse or partner you are a victim of sexual abuse. After letting out the secret and not being rejected or abandoned, you might sigh in relief, assume everything has been dealt with, and believe it will never have to be thought about or spoken of again. Unfortunately, it rarely works out that way.

When I refer to reaching some level of security in life prior to having the denial lift, it is important to remember that stability is relative. For one person this might mean having a good income, an understanding spouse, a network of supportive friends, and a good therapist. For another, whose spouse is emotionally, physically, and/or sexually abusive, it might mean simply having a secure and supportive job environment. One client of mine who was in her early forties decided to confront her own incest history, her husband's sexual abuse of their daughter, and his abuse of her. She came from a family characterized by generations of incest. Following her treatment for alcoholism she got a good job and the layers of denial rapidly began to peel away. Once awareness of her own incest started to surface, she quickly broke through the denial covering her daughter's abuse and ended her marriage. Her denial was no longer necessary once she felt ready and safe enough to look at the facts involving her own life, feel her intense pain, and move forward.

Intellectual Understanding

Early stages of recovery are often characterized by an intellectual approach. This is an effort to "think it through quickly" so we can put it behind us. You might do this entirely on your own, or you might seek help from books, magazines, articles, or television documentaries. Regardless of the approach, this is an important attempt to address your mental split by trying to make sense of the past. It does provide some healing. Many questions can be answered during this stage and you can begin to comprehend that you weren't responsible for the incest. Until destructive thinking like, "I made Daddy do it" is examined, correcting a faulty thought process cannot move forward. Intellectual analysis creates the seductive illusion that, after rationally understanding the psychological factors of the incest, you can forgive your parents and simply let it go. This approach feels wonderfully safe because it uses the familiar mind/emotion/body splits and allows you to ignore difficult, painful feelings.

Most victims carry a lot of anger inside, and intellectualizing it seems a safe approach. This shouldn't be surprising. Many of us lived with a great deal of overt and covert anger and rage within our families of origin, and we understand just how destructive these feelings can be. Since we may have never learned how to release anger, it makes sense that the last thing we want to do is face our own anger and risk subjecting others to the same explosive rage we witnessed in one or both of our parents. But it's not just your anger that's bubbling around inside you. There also are many feelings you probably don't know how to process appropriately. It's very common to be depressed and totally unaware that this is a cover for many confusing and repressed feelings, including anger, grief, sadness, shame, and a profound sense of abandonment and betrayal.

The intellectual approach may seem to be a safe answer to your emotions. It's appealing to try to wrap it all up neatly by telling yourself your father didn't know any better, he was a sick man, your mother was too weak to protect you because of her victim role as a woman, your parents did the best they could, and so on. It's appealing because the logical outgrowth of this reasoning is that you can quickly forgive your parents and forget what took place. You want this to work because it's tidy. It allows you to go on as though nothing happened, telling yourself you really do have a warm and loving family of origin, ignoring the effects of the abuse. This approach doesn't even require talking with anyone from your family of origin about it. Unfortunately, the cognitive portion of the recovery process isn't enough.

Cognitive understanding is a necessary and helpful part of recovery, but it's only one part. Doing the intellectual work often allows you to settle down for a time—perhaps many years—before something sets off the need to do more work on incest issues. Sometimes this is a delayed realization that the depression never totally lifted after cognitive psychotherapy. Other times it may be triggered by your children when they reach the age you were when you were abused, or by having a spouse who wants more freedom and frequency in your sexual relationship, or perhaps by the frustration and shame triggered while trying to succeed at school or in a job.

Emotional Readiness

We frequently begin to deal with the emotional portion of recovery by acknowledging that

19

life "feels bad." We get angry and blame our parents for our struggles. It's at this point that we forget all those tidy, intellectual explanations about what happened. We allow ourselves to feel our resentment and anger about how we were treated. It's no longer very important whether there was a "good reason" for the incest; it shouldn't have happened and someone out there should have protected us. From the feeling part of us come the angry questions about where the protective adults were, and where the hell was God when all of this was going on?

At this point we rely on our mind/emotion/body splits to get to the feelings. We have to forget about our heads for a while to feel free enough to experience our feelings. Integrating our thoughts with our feelings through our bodies comes later. It's okay to use these splits long enough to discover our emotions and become comfortable with having them. After we come to know and accept ourselves as feeling people, we can add the thoughts that match our feelings.

You Can't Ignore the Past

I have never seen an abuse victim heal without dealing with his or her past. We have all tried very hard to cope and heal by using reality therapy and by keeping focused on today. Many of my clients had seen other therapists who did not allow them to talk freely about the past. By the time I saw them, they felt they were shameful failures because they were unable to forget the past. They were made to feel they were living in the past and feeling a lot of self-pity. They wondered if they were wasting their lives—that maybe they just did not want to accept the responsibility of getting well.

Incest survivors are rarely stuck in self-pity. Someone is stuck in self-pity when they only want to use the past as an excuse to stay the way they are. Self-pity as an approach to life might sound like this: "What do you expect from me? After all, I was raised by an alcoholic parent who sexually abused me." This horrible history becomes a justification and a free ticket to be a victim who dependently lives off the world, rather than an adult who uses personal strengths to put forth best efforts.

Feeling Old Pain

Taking the time to grieve and feel sorry and sad for all your losses does not bar you from continuing to move forward. It really is possible to invest in today and tomorrow even while you're feeling pain from the past. In fact, feeling that old pain is the only truly effective way to begin moving forward. Otherwise, we use too much energy to repress the pain and that energy isn't available to help us heal.

The insight gained from past experience is very freeing. Our choices multiply when we face old fears. When we understand all the fear inside us, we can free ourselves to live differently. We no longer have to walk around with a lump in our throat once we realize that we resisted crying because someone once threatened to lock us up if we released the tears. We come to understand that conditions are different now and it is safe to cry. This unhooking from past trauma and expressing emotions that were previously blocked is a powerful experience.

You don't have to remember everything about your abuse to feel healthy and whole. You only need to be open to facing those memories that your psyche sends to the surface. The memory may be rising to the conscious level because your body still has the emotional trauma left in its tissues and this needs to be released before you can be free of chronic muscle tension.

The memory may also be coming up because you have something to learn from it to help you move forward in a particular area of your life. Your story unfolds so you can identify your hooks and blocks. You can feel validated that you are not crazy because the facts support the feelings you have struggled with. Understanding the past can help you make sense of problems such as incapacitating fear, sexual dysfunction, being exploited sexually as an adult, alcohol and drug abuse, compulsive eating, induced vomiting, suicidal thinking, and the like. You didn't just decide to have these problems, nor did you get them because you are an irresponsible person. The explanation lies in the past. Understanding the past offers you the hope of escaping the shameful messages of unworthiness you took in as a child.

Reliving the past is a special way of handling memories. In this process you regress back to the age and situation consistent with the memory. I believe this is the most effective way to release the emotion, and without this release, the memory may never seem totally believable or real. It is the emotional dimension that fills out the complete picture and permits an integration of mind, emotion, and body. I have had thoughts that suggested my memories were only a reflection of my own crazy imagination. But when I gave myself permission to feel and release the feelings attached to the memories, I found myself screaming. If those memories weren't real, they would not have generated such powerful terror and rage.

Channeling Our Feelings

During this time we might walk around openly angry and abrasive toward others, perhaps jumping on a bandwagon or two to fight various injustices and abuses in the world. In spite of our depression we may feel energized by releasing some of the anger, speaking out for underdogs and setting things right. But we need to know what we are really angry about before this expression of feeling will be very helpful. Emoting feelings all over the place has no lasting healing effect unless we connect the emotion to some cognitive awareness.

During this angry portion of our recovery we can be unpleasant to be around. We don't want to look closely at the past, so we often blindly spill our anger on anyone except the abuser. The risk is that we can become stuck and fail to move through to resolution. Some of the bitter angry elderly are incest victims who never got a chance or never took the opportunity to work through their abusive pasts.

Attaching Anger to the Correct Source

It is important to understand that this angry blaming phase is neither right nor wrong; it just is. If you are currently stuck in this stage, ask yourself why you are so angry. This may allow you to accept that you are shifting from a purely cognitive level of dealing with your issues to a more feeling level. This is an encouraging sign that the integration of thought and feeling, which is essential for full recovery, is underway.

Facing the Flashbacks

Flashbacks are typical in recovery. Memories from many years ago suddenly begin to surface. These memories usually surface in fragments, both during dream states and when we are fully awake. Most often we see a brief flash of a picture without awareness of what it is about or why we see it. Sometimes, instead of a picture, a stray thought might be followed in a few days by a picture or dream which expands on the original thought. It's common to respond to this with fear and panic. We feel confused, out of control, even crazy. This is a time for self-trust and the courage to explore how these flashbacks are connected to reality. However, many of us tend to assume we're making things up. When reality eventually sets in, we may go through an identity crisis. After living many years believing we know who we are and what we have experienced, this perception is shattered and we feel overwhelmed with confusion about where we have been and what we know. Shame-based people are generally raised to believe that who they are is determined by what they know and don't know, so confusion about these issues automatically generates confusion about personal identity.

Remembering through the Body

We also relive memories through the body. When our repression is starting to crack, our bodies may tell some of the story by re-experiencing our physical pain. Many survivors experience intensified lower back pain or pelvic discomfort while reliving memories of childhood sexual abuse. Vaginal or rectal pain, as well as choking and gagging sensations, are common, depending upon whether the person was abused vaginally, anally, or orally. The physical manifestations of incest are examined closely in the next chapters. Sometimes a style of clothing which tightens around the wrists or ankles can trigger memories of incest that involved bondage.

Sexual excitement in response to certain stimuli associated with incest can also trigger the flow of repressed memories. I have worked with people who felt intense shame and believed they were demented because thinking about or being in church aroused them. These clients were abused sexually as a form of punishment for inappropriate behavior in church when they were little girls. Fear, anger, and sadness can serve as openings into repressed memories, provided these feelings can be explored in a safe environment.

Integration

You need to trust your mind, feelings, and body as valid sources of truth. Ultimately, and despite the poor role models in incestuous families, your recovery process will involve integrating these three aspects of your identity. This is not easy since you were most likely shamed into becoming fragmented by family members who did not have a clue as to how to handle experiences of healthy integrated living. This integration is generally manageable if you can be patient with yourself and avoid feeling crazy just because you're still at a spot where your mind, emotions, and body do not match.

Spirituality

Recovery also requires us to face the issue of spirituality, and to begin integrating ourselves with the universe and God or our Higher Power. We need to understand our purpose on earth, to feel content with the notion of mankind's worthiness, and ultimately to confront the final depths of our shame. Coming to grips with our spirituality entails discovering that we are truly worthy of unconditional love. It involves filling up within to heal the shameful and unbonded infant inside us. This is often difficult and painful because we must confront the shameful feeling that we are unworthy. It's like a storm that eventually carries us to a calm and peaceful place. We might navigate our way through this storm alone, with a member of the clergy, or with a psychotherapist. Books, such as *When Bad Things Happen To Good People* by Harold S. Kushner and *The Road Less Traveled* by M. Scott Peck, M.D., also can be helpful.

Integrating Our Spiritual Being

We are, first, spiritual beings. Our spiritual beings come into our bodies, thereby making us human beings. Our minds and bodies are tools that allow us to accomplish goals, but we are not our minds and we are not our bodies. Our minds give us the power of thought, allowing us to interpret and make sense of what surrounds us. Our bodies house our emotions, allowing us to feel in response to our thoughts. Our bodies also permit us to move around so we can take actions to release feelings and accomplish tasks. Successful recovery from the impact of abuse requires that we develop the ability to quietly go within ourselves and get in touch with our spiritual being. This spiritual being comes from a place of objectivity, wisdom, compassion, and spriritual love. Phrases such as "relying on intuition" and "coming from the heart" refer to our spiritual being.

Our spiritual being has the capacity to listen to our thoughts, feelings, and bodies and integrate these parts with childhood and adult experiences to help us make a wise decision. It will know if our fear is due to imminent danger, or if the fear is coming from a chidhood memory that does not pertain to today and is only serving to block us from current goals. Integration of our spiritual being with our human body and mind represents healing of the mind/emotion/body splits. Our human parts allow us to fully experience the beauty of a mountain scene, hear the glorious sound of music, feel the smooth sensation of silk, taste the sweetness of French silk pie, smell the lilacs in spring, and cry and jump for joy when excited. Our challenge is to unite our human parts with our spiritual being.

Meditation is one of the most effective ways of accessing our spiritual being. It provides welcome distance from the details of life and allows us to clear blockages, focus on the truly significant, and establish direction for the future. Some people mentally place themselves on the top of a mountain where they are able to talk with a wise old person. Others see themselves floating on a cloud talking to themselves or to God. Betty asks to hear from her guardian angel when she needs clarity and direction, while Barb prays to her Higher Power. I encourage you to experiment, either on your own or with the help of a real or imagined guide, with various mental images as a way of discovering how you can best get in touch with your spiritual being. Remember to concentrate on opening up your breathing and slowing down. Trust yourself to have the wisdom to discover how best to get your answers. You will know when you have contacted your spiritual being because you will feel a quiet tranquility within. You may not always like what you hear, but you will experience the acceptance that the information or direction revealed to you is correct.

Grieving the Loss

For most incest survivors, the primary loss is family of origin relationships. This is true whether we decide to terminate relationships or restructure them. We feel deep grief when we let go of the illusion that we are from a normal healthy family. Our inner child goes through intense grief while struggling with this loss. This part of us intuitively understands what we needed from our family, and begins to grieve when it realizes how badly those needs were neglected. We can't replace our original family, if this is what we elect to do, without first grieving this loss. There is a dual loss here: the real family and the ideal family that never was. We will grieve periodically over the years in many ways and at many levels. We may be successful at finding substitute parents, siblings, and grandparents —and it is very healthy and helpful to our healing to do so—but this won't erase the loss that occurs when our needs aren't met within our family of origin. This grief is difficult, but it is unavoidable if recovery is to be complete.

Acceptance

Grief is a natural process which allows us to feel, and eventually recover from, loss. It frequently starts while our denial is largely intact, creating a volatile time of anger, pain, anxiety, blame, and confusion. This is often followed by depression, disorientation, and detachment during which we look into ourselves to process all that has happened. Then we begin to accept that the incest happened. We often feel stronger for having gone through the grieving process and believe we have more to give back to life as a result of surviving our trauma.

Acceptance is not saying it is okay the incest happened. *Incest is never okay.* Acceptance means acknowledging that it occurred, knowing this fact cannot be changed, and feeling ready to take all our acquired strengths and move forward. Acceptance cannot be forced; it is a natural outcome that results from mental sorting, feeling, body releasing, and behavioral changing.

Forgiveness

The final stage of acceptance for incest survivors involves forgiveness. This in no way implies that we are saying the abuse was acceptable. Forgiveness means finding a way to be as finished as possible with the pain and anger in order to free up energy for other things. Forgiveness allows us to move forward.

Remember, forgiveness is for you. It is not for the perpetrator. It means letting go of the past, tearing down the bars which have formed the psychological prison that kept us captive for so many years. Forgiveness, as with acceptance, can never be forced. Trying to forgive too early in the recovery process will only reinforce our mind/emotion/body splits, thereby delaying the experience of pain and anger. Forgiveness will follow, rather than precede, all the difficult work of recovery.

Our forgiveness does not suggest anything about our future relationship with our abuser. It is merely a transformation that takes place within us and permits us to step out of the past. Once we have forgiven acts of the past, we still must decide what we wish to establish for the future. Part of what makes this process empowering is that it doesn't require anything from the abuser. It reverses the power relationship between survivor and abuser by allowing the survivor to be in control. We can use our growth and perception to decide to let go and move forward. Forgiveness allows us to discard the victim role. When we forgive, we actively make the choice to stop diverting so much energy into staying angry with our abuser.

Moving Forward

Recovery involves not only pain and grieving, but also personal integration and positive change. We gradually evaluate our relationships with friends, work associates, spouses, and family of origin to determine whether they are capable of growth and enhancement. If not, we may need to replace some or all of these relationships. Those who are unable or unwilling to strike a healthy balance between giving and taking may have to be set aside in favor of people who value us sufficiently to put energy into maintaining a quality relationship.

Healthy people move into and out of relationships over time. Some of these may be long-lasting while others, such as job-related friendships, may be brief. It's important to trust yourself and believe you will find a way to have enough people in your life to satisfy your needs. With this understanding, you won't be dependent on one group of people. Ending a relationship brings grief, but it also opens up a fresh opportunity to begin another relationship with a different person. There can be fear, but also fulfillment. If you are willing to take some risks to move through the grief and the fear, you can open yourself to a more satisfying and complete life than you've been able to imagine. This is what incest recovery is all about.

2

Physical Damage

In addition to the psychological damage that results from sexual abuse, there is frequently a physical cost as well. Sometimes the physical damage is obvious at the outset of the abuse. Sometimes it is not evident until we reach a point in life where we feel safe enough to slow down, come into our bodies, and develop increased body awareness. The stress which accompanies years of memory repression may give rise to health problems. Physical problems may also develop during psychotherapy as we confront the reality of the abuse and engage in the intense painful work required for healing.

Psychosomatic Illnesses

Psychosomatic conditions are real stress-related

illnesses. Most of us are strongly programmed not to burden others with our problems. We are so ashamed of our bodies that we are not inclined to seek attention through their ailments. Psychosomatic illnesses are *not* imaginary or exaggerated physical problems for which we hope to receive attention.

Because we typically repress our trauma and its associated emotions, we are vulnerable to stress-related illnesses. These include migraines, ulcers, constipation, muscle spasms, back pain, bladder and vaginal infections, colitis, TMJ (Temporomandibular Joint or Tight Muscular Jaw) and others. The longer we hold in our pain, the more likely it is that our bodies will slowly begin to fall apart.

Not every incest survivor is damaged in the ways discussed in this chapter, nor does this material represent a complete listing of potential physical problems, but these typical patterns of physical damage make it clear that damage from sexual abuse frequently extends beyond the psychological. The following checklist will help you identify some of the ways in which incest may

have affected you physically. Ask yourself if any
of these statements describe your body.

- I have deformities or scars, and parts of my
  body don't function properly as a direct result
  of my sexual abuse.
- My body does not seem to handle stress
  very well.
- I sometimes experience tunnel vision and
  numbness, show a fearful face, and feel a tight
  squeezing sensation around the crown of
  my head.
- I feel exhausted, have an acidic stomach, and
  am bothered by poor digestion.
- I have repeated yeast infections, feel lethargic
  and depressed, have trouble with headaches
  and skin problems, and suffer from aching
  joints and muscles.
- I have cold or canker sores and/or genital her-
  pes that I cannot seem to keep under control.
- I experience intense premenstrual syndrome
  (PMS).
- I am sterile.
- I have endometriosis.

- I have urinary incontinence.
- I am bothered by severe constipation.
- I experience chronic muscle constriction, such as painful knots in my upper back.
- I do not know how to take very good care of myself, and I ignore my health.
- I have tension or migraine headaches.
- I experience TMJ.
- I have dental problems.
- For males only: I feel a constant painful pressure in my genitals that is relieved only by an orgasm.
- For males only: My orgasms leave me feeling physically unsatisfied.

Perhaps the most obvious physical health problems are those that have such an immediate and direct connection to the abuse that no reasonable person would dispute the origin of the damage. Generally, these are structural deformities such as broken bones or a damaged pelvis.

Many survivors suffer chronic pain in the lower back, pelvic region, and legs. Sometimes pain in these areas is a result of structural damage such as stretched pelvic ligaments caused by having intercourse at a young age. At other times it is a result of chronic muscle spasms and constrictions caused by habitual tightening of lower back and pelvic muscles. Physical therapy, chiropractic care, osteopathic treatment, massage, and yoga seem to be most effective in alleviating this pain.

Post-traumatic Shock Syndrome

Dr. Karl Kirsch, a psychiatrist who specializes in the physical effects of emotional trauma, believes that shock is a natural by-product of all forms of abuse. A person in shock will have a startled terrorized look on his or her face, eyes that appear glassy and blank, and may seem to be not fully present. Sufferers experience disorientation, tunnel vision, and a constricting sensation around the top of the head. Hyperventilation may occur in extreme cases, or shallow breathing alternating with holding of the breath in milder cases. Heart palpitations will occur in response to the adrenaline that is released in preparation for fight or flight behavior.

Many incest survivors experience intense

flashbacks during psychotherapy. We start to integrate memory fragments concerning our incest and consequently become aware of shock symptoms.

Treating Shock. Shock can be readily treated. The first step is to learn to recognize your symptoms. As mentioned above, you may feel a tight band squeezing around the crown of your head, you may experience tunnel vision where everything is focused straight ahead while everything else seems far away and surrounded by a cloudy haze, and your legs and feet may become numb.

To bring back body awareness, inhale slowly through your nose, pulling the air all the way down into your stomach and abdomen. Then exhale through your mouth. To help get a better feel for this process, you might start by placing one hand on your stomach and the other on your chest. If your diaphragm and abdomen expand, your chest should also expand, thereby giving your entire torso a complete breath. Slow deep breaths are best. Small quick breaths might induce dizziness from hyperventilation. This slow breathing pattern can also be used to reduce anxiety and control panic attacks. Shock is an intensified version of anxiety and panic.

Wiggling your toes and feet, patting your legs, and rubbing your feet with your hands or against the floor will help bring back sensation. Opening your eyes wide, perhaps several times, will help clear your head.

You can use a specific technique to alleviate the discomfort associated with the tight band around the head. Place your hands on the upper sides of your head and squeeze, holding this grip for a few seconds. Move your hands to other spots around the crown of your head and repeat. It may seem as if this would make the problem worse, but it is effective.

Most of the time it is not necessary to do all the steps. For example, if you feel a need to clear your vision while driving, simply open your eyes very wide, take several slow deep breaths, and wiggle your toes. Your vision should clear quickly. On particularly bad days you may need to repeat these steps many times.

Shock can easily become a way of life. When we are tired, hungry, or upset, we may unconsciously go into shock. Becoming aware of the pattern of situations or stressors that triggers acute episodes of shock syndrome helps us identify what is happening within our bodies. Although shock can help temporarily cushion us against a physical or psychological blow, we do not usually require this kind of cushioning. In most situations it is dangerous to be in a state where you are unaware of immediate risks.

Incest survivors need to understand it is safe to feel our childhood experiences. We no longer need to be in a state of shock to survive. We can find a safe place with a person we trust who will allow us to feel protected as we come into our feelings about our abuse. We do not have to put our lives on hold or function ineffectively while healing from incest. Simple training will do a great deal to keep us alert, present in our bodies, and safe.

Overworked Adrenal and Digestive Systems

Chronic shock can produce significant physical illness, in part because it leads to overworking of the adrenal system. This overstimulates production of other chemicals within the body. As with most overburdened systems, the adrenal glands, stomach, and pancreas eventually burn out. This leads to chronic exhaustion and poor digestion. Gastritis, diarrhea, and ulcers can occur. Bloating, severe stomach pains, regurgitation, and sharp gas pains that radiate up into the diaphragm and cause lower chest pain are other common symptoms of damage in this area.

Severe constipation can result from tightly holding the pelvic and rectal muscles, a behavior common among incest victims. Perforated bowels or bowel obstructions are potential consequences of chronic constipation. The purpose of the bowels is to remove toxins from the body. When the toxins remain in the bowels for an extended time, they may be absorbed into the bloodstream and carried to the brain, usually resulting in headaches and mental fuzziness.

Treating Constipation and Digestive Problems. It is important to deal with chronic constipation slowly and gently. Never use harsh laxatives as they may tear the bowel lining, which is already likely to be inflamed. A high fiber diet, plenty of caffeine-free liquids, and a reasonable exercise program are generally the most effective ways to treat constipation and maintain healthy bowels.

A high fiber diet that omits liquids may produce a bulk mass that simply adds to the constipation problem. Caffeine draws liquid to the bladder rather than the bowels, limiting the amount of liquid available for softening the stool. A breakfast that combines fruit juice with high fiber toast or cereal, or perhaps a bran muffin, can serve to stimulate the peristaltic movement of the bowels. Also, if we expect our bodies to work actively for us, then we need to put them in motion through a regular, moderate, exercise program. It is not necessary to impersonate Jane Fonda. Taking rapid walks several times a week will do wonders over time.

Many of us have serious difficulties with constipation but consider it a trivial and embarrassing problem. Breaking through the shame to bring up the subject with a busy doctor can be difficult, especially if our shame incorporates the fear of being a burden. But we must find a way to do it.

Treatment for digestive problems involves the same attention to diet, liquids, and exercise. In addition, your body may need to rest and heal without the pressure of constant chemical production. Dietary supplements of hydrochloric acid, acidophilus, and pancreatic enzymes are often prescribed by holistic doctors. Generally, the body will begin production of these chemicals again after a while. Recovery can be slow, so be patient with yourself.

Systemic Candidiasis

Chronic shock can lead to another physical condition known as systemic candidiasis, which is a disease of the immune system. The immune system produces the antibodies necessary to the ongoing battle against unhealthy germs. It is the function of the antibodies to neutralize certain bacteria so the body can handle them.

Candida albicans is a body yeast that grows on skin and mucous membranes, most commonly in the vaginal tract. When it grows to the point where vaginal itching and drainage occur, a yeast infection requiring treatment has developed.

Extensive use of broad spectrum antibiotics, which attack all sorts of bacteria as opposed to a specific type, may lead to growth of *candida albicans* throughout the mucous membranes of the body. This will interfere with the body's ability to block toxins from crossing through the membranes and entering the bloodstream. Since female incest survivors frequently have histories of various infections that are typically treated with antibiotics, we are at risk for development of this disorder. Prolonged use of tetracycline, birth control pills, and various hormone therapies also appear to predispose people to systemic candidiasis.

It's a vicious cycle. Direct body abuse, multiple infections, extensive use of antibiotics, birth control pills, and poor diet all may contribute to break down the immune system. Consequently, we have a greater susceptibility to other infections that are also likely to be treated with broad spectrum antibiotics.

Systemic candidiasis is a psychosomatic illness, but as mentioned before, this does not mean we've imagined the condition. It means our stress is so intense that an actual breakdown in the body has taken place. Under normal conditions where the adrenal and immune systems are not overtaxed, the body will be able to take care of excess yeast. Our bodies can handle a great deal, but if we are in a state of chronic shock for years without significant relief we can expect our bodies to collapse eventually.

Systemic candidiasis is most typically diagnosed by completing a questionnaire that outlines a particular symptom profile. This questionnaire can be found in *The Yeast Connection* by William Crook, M.D. Another excellent source of information is *The Missing Diagnosis* by C.O. Truss. This book is more scholarly than Crook's book, and includes research results.

Crook points out that systemic candidiasis symptoms include extreme fatigue or lethargy, depression, inability to concentrate, headaches, skin problems (hives, athlete's foot, nail fungus infections, jock itch, psoriasis, chronic skin rashes), gastrointestinal symptoms (constipation, abdominal pain, diarrhea, gas, or bloating), vaginitis and vaginal infections, aching joints, weak or painful muscles, respiratory difficulties, hyperactivity, and recurrent ear problems. True, these symptoms could suggest all sorts of illnesses; however, systemic candidiasis is characterized by the simultaneous presence of several of these symptoms. The presence of only one or two of them does not justify a diagnosis of this disorder. The symptoms must be evaluated in conjunction with medical history and past and present life stressors.

Treating Systemic Candidiasis. Effective treatment involves a change in diet, more appropriate stress management, and in some cases, an antifungal medication. To ease our recovery, we must slow down our lifestyle dramatically. We must reduce our perfectionist expectations, eat well, drink plenty of liquids, get adequate rest, exercise moderately, and maintain a healthy balance between work and fun. Dr. Crook's book also outlines the commonly prescribed antifungal medications used to treat this disorder.

If your body is in poor shape there may be some limits to how much you can exercise. If exercise energizes you it should become part of your regular schedule. If you are drained and exhausted afterward, you probably can't handle it yet. Nap rather than exercise if that is what you need. Your body will tell you what you need if you listen to it.

The most effective emotional treatment for systemic candidiasis is to stop blaming yourself for the fact that your body has broken down. You may be ashamed that you aren't strong enough and emotionally together enough to avoid having your past get to you. But anyone subjected to the abuse and stress that incest victims have endured will have a physiological breakdown. You must be kind to yourself and understand that you've simply reacted to excessive stress. Be patient and accepting of whatever state your body is in at present. This is most likely to occur if you've given yourself permission to complain for a while that your body doesn't work very well.

Premenstrual Syndrome

Premenstrual syndrome (PMS) is directly related to stress. PMS involves an uncomfortable shift within the body as it prepares itself for the menstrual period. The more stress you are experiencing, the more you will feel this shift. The intense stress connected with recovery can contribute to the development of, or the worsening of, PMS. Common symptoms include headaches, fluid retention, abdominal bloating, irritability and mood swings, compulsive eating, cravings for sweets, salt, and chocolate, fatigue, depression, leg muscle cramps, and backaches.

Treatment of PMS. Treatment for this disorder requires that we reduce our intake of salt, sweets, and caffeine. Exercise can help with depression and fluid retention. Vitamin B complex reduces mood swings and fatigue. Calcium and magnesium help alleviate muscle cramps. Vitamin C reduces fluid retention. Some PMS formula vitamins combine these items along with other minerals that become depleted during menstruation.

Plotting your menstrual cycle on a calendar can be helpful. Pace yourself with tasks. Putting a little distance in relationships when symptoms are particularly intense can help us avoid hurting those we care about and disrupting our relationships.

Infertility

Some women are so damaged as a result of violent incest, self-mutilation, or small body size at the time the abuse occurred that they become infertile. Sometimes the fallopian tubes are damaged from pelvic inflammatory disease (PID) occurring at an early age. Many survivors who vaginally self-mutilate are unable to bear children. I have worked with women who have psychologically shut down their hormone production for a number of years to avoid having periods. This is how they dealt with the shame relating to sex and their overwhelming fear of pregnancy. A combination of psychotherapy and hormone treatment by an endocrinologist is usually enough to correct this problem. If you miss your period for more than three months at any time during your menstruating years, and you are not pregnant, consult a gynecologist or an endocrinologist.

Endometriosis

Many incest survivors suffer from endometriosis, a condition in which the special tissue within the uterus that bleeds during the menstrual period grows outside of the uterus. If you have a history of chronic pain associated with your period, you need to consult a gynecologist to rule out endometriosis or to receive appropriate treatment for this disorder.

Urinary Incontinence

Some incest survivors experience regular urinary incontinence, most often connected to panic attacks. Therapy, in combination with mental imagery focusing on controlling the urge to urinate long enough to get to a bathroom, can help.

Chronic Muscle Constriction

We frequently respond to the invasion of our bodies by unconsciously tightening various muscle groups. Once these muscles become tightened, it is possible to leave the body and move into the head, thereby eliminating the need to feel distracting sensations. Over the years this constriction can come to feel natural.

We can most effectively deal with this by deliberate and concentrated focus on opening up affected parts of the body. For example, if the muscles of the buttocks, anus, and rectum have been chronically constricted, squeezing these muscles and then relaxing them while pushing down can be quite helpful in relieving tension. This exercise, when done inconspicuously while going about daily activities, will train you to be more fully present in your body, assist you in recognizing when you're constricting these muscles, help develop better muscle tone, and put you in touch with the signals your body sends when it wants to be emptied. Similar approaches can be used with other troublesome muscle groups.

Headaches

Most headaches not related to sinus problems start with tension in the upper back, shoulders, and neck. Breathing deeply is our natural way of opening up constricted muscles and blood vessels. Gently stretching these muscles with yoga exercises and massage also can help a great deal. By releasing repressed emotions, and continuing to release emotions as they arise, we practice the best prevention for headaches.

Many incest survivors suffer migraine headaches. Although we know migraines are a vascular disorder treatable with medication, we also know the vascular constriction that causes the headache, acute sensitivity to light, nausea, and vomiting is worsened by tension-induced muscular constriction. Consequently, the treatment approach outlined above can also help in managing migraine headaches.

Tight Muscular Jaw (Temporomandibular Joint)

In our attempt to hold in our screams of terror and rage over the years, we may have chronically clamped down our jaws, leading to muscle constriction and spasm. Some of us have subconsciously clamped down our jaws to avoid telling our secrets or to prevent anyone from sexually violating our mouths again. This can gradually lock our mouths closed, creating jaw pain. Mouthpieces, physical therapy, massage, and surgery are all used to treat TMJ. Dentists, orthopedists, and chiropractors are the professionals who typically treat this disorder.

Dental Problems

Receiving poor dental care due to neglectful parents, suffering damage at the time of abuse, and experiencing TMJ all contribute to chronic dental problems. Repressed feelings often cause us to grind our teeth while we sleep. This unconscious effort to process emotional pain can cause badly worn teeth and gum disease. Chronic bulimia also contributes to serious dental problems because the vomiting of stomach acid erodes the enamel which protects teeth. Changes in pH factor within the mouth can also cause gum disease. Consult with your dentist or an orthodontist about treatment for dental problems.

Healing Process

Quality parenting includes education about health care. Incest families often leave significant gaps in knowledge about things like how to take a temperature, how to medicate a fever, when to stay home sick from work, and other basic measures of health care. We generally believe we should know more than we do about taking care of our bodies, so our feelings of shame and inadequacy are intensified. It is potentially healing to realize that these gaps are the natural result of parental neglect.

Whether you're a man or a woman, and no matter how old you are, you need to be patient and kind to yourself. Your body has been abused by others as well as by you. As a result, it has been working overtime for many years. Healing involves acceptance and a commitment to giving your body what it has needed for a long time: adequate rest, healthy food, appropriate exercise, kind healing thoughts, and mental images aimed at physical recovery.

3

Mental Imagery

I use a great deal of mental imagery in my work with incest survivors. I do this because I believe in the importance of the connections among mind, emotion, and body. When we can visualize something positive for ourselves, it makes room for it to happen. When we are unable to perceive positive events taking place, then we set the stage so good things don't pan out. It generally works best when we take bits and pieces from many ideas and create our own integrated approaches to emotional healing. What proves helpful for one person may need to be modified for someone else.

While learning to do mental imagery, you will likely discover your primary way of relating to the world. Most people have a dominant sense—vision, touch, smell, taste, or hearing. Keep in mind there is no right or wrong way to image the world; whatever way you perceive the universe is just fine. The only requirement for using mental imagery within your healing process is that you are able to create an image in your mind.

To learn which sense or senses dominates your perception of the world, pay attention to the words you use. Since I am strongest visually (sight) and kinesthetically (touch), I will often say things such as: "Yes, I can *see* your point" or, "Yes, I *feel* strongly about that." I am not likely to say, "Yes, I *hear* your point." I believe I am oriented to the world in this way primarily because of my incest experience. I shut down my auditory sense in order to keep from having to hear all the bad sounds in my home, but I kept my eyes open and focused to pick up on potential danger. I also developed an ability to sense what was in the air without having to hear all the violence and verbal abuse. When you come across words such as *picture* or *see* in this book, please keep in mind this reflects my natural tendency. Feel free to image in your own way.

In this chapter and in many of the chapters

that follow, we will explore your abilities with mental imagery. This will be done by presenting material within the chapter text and then listing specific imaging exercises that amplify that material at the end of the chapter. These exercises are presented in a straightforward step-by-step format. I suggest you read through each exercise completely and then set aside the book and try it. It may be necessary for you to reread some of this material, so take your time. You can also record the exercises into a tape recorder to eliminate the distraction of having to open your eyes to read the various steps. If you elect to do this, remember to speak slowly so there will be enough time available to create and feel the images as you listen to your voice. People who have been shamed for using their imagination may experience some initial difficulty with these exercises. If this is true for you, simply remember the more you work at developing your imagination, the easier it will become to create images.

Playfulness while learning to do mental imagery is important. When you are bored, allow yourself to drift off and daydream, but this time pay particular attention to the images which arise. Another practice method involves spontaneously creating mental images of all sorts of things, such as numbers, objects, places you have been, faces of people you know, and animals. Include in these images such details as color, size, texture, and smell. This can be a wonderful game when you're bored.

Mental Imagery Exercises

* Settle back in a comfortable chair, gently close your eyes, and imagine a flower. Pay attention to size, color, shape, smell, and texture. Hold this image as long as you can.

* After you feel reasonably skilled at imaging the flower with your eyes closed, do the same thing with your eyes open. This is generally more difficult, but it can be done with practice. It's very useful to be able to image both with open and closed eyes.

4

Coming Back into Your Body

The more stress we feel when we're tired, confronted with painful emotions, or involved in threatening or abusive situations, the more we are inclined to leave our bodies. The key is to recognize what it feels like to be out-of-body and which situations are especially likely to produce an out-of-body state. This helps us avoid placing ourselves in these situations, and it allows us to get out of such circumstances more quickly when we cannot avoid them entirely. Learning new coping skills for dealing with painful emotions can also be helpful for keeping us in our bodies.

Leaving the body is a survival mechanism that is quite helpful for a person who is a true victim and unable to change a dangerous environment. While this helplessness applies to children who are being abused, it does not typically apply to adults. With some exceptions (rape is one), adults have choices when it comes to staying in or leaving abusive conditions. If a grizzly bear is about to attack, you might want to leave your body, but it's better to stay fully present so you can problem-solve. If you're totally trapped and being shredded by the bear's claws, it is then helpful to leave your body to escape the pain. As adults, how often are we really trapped? Usually we simply assume we are trapped and rely on the familiar habit of leaving the body to avoid dealing with a troublesome situation.

Physical activity and direct contact with the earth are excellent ways of becoming grounded within ourselves and curtailing our out-of-body experiences. Walking moves energy down into the lower half of the body and at the same time draws energy up from the earth. Attending to routine tasks such as washing the floor pulls our focus back to the here and now and also moves energy throughout the body. Working in the yard, especially gardening, is another effective technique for focusing on the moment as we draw from the earth's positive energy. We can allow ourselves to feel particularly connected with the earth by gardening without shoes, socks, or gloves.

Getting Grounded

One of the most basic ways mental imagery can help healing is by allowing us to feel more focused and less scattered in life. When we are ungrounded, we feel disconnected and out of control; when we are grounded, we feel like our feet are solidly planted within the universe. To benefit from a grounding exercise, you must be solidly focused in your body. There are some techniques to help you with this. Say your full name out loud. Take slow, deep breaths while looking around and taking in your surroundings. Be aware of the feeling in your feet and legs by moving your toes. Just being able to mentally visualize your feet and legs isn't enough—you must be able to feel them and know you are connected to them, know that they are living parts of you.

Once you feel you are fully present within your body, a simple exercise as noted below can effectively center or ground you within your body. It is an excellent way to start each day as it can help you feel more energized and more stable. It can be done as often as you wish whenever you feel the need to ground yourself. I suggest you avoid doing it before you go to bed because the extra energy might keep you awake.

Developing the skills to bring your being into your body and ground it there can work wonders to heal that part of you which feels disconnected from the world and from yourself. Now that the sexual abuse has stopped, it is finally safe to "come home" within yourself.

Mental Imagery Exercises

* Sit in a straight chair with your feet planted flat on the floor. Close your eyes and visualize a solid cord connected to the bottom of your left foot and another cord connected to the bottom of your right foot. Now see each cord going down through the floor and into the ground, all the way down to the core or center of the earth. Imagine the earth's energy flowing up through these cords to your feet. Allow the bot-

toms of your feet to open and permit the energy to flow up your legs to the bottom of your spine. Now allow this energy to move up to the top of your spine, which is located in the center of the back side of your brain. You may feel the energy coming up as you visualize it or you may simply see it. Both experiences are common and they accomplish the same purpose.

5

Finding a Spiritual Protector

It's often very helpful when you are processing abuse memories to use mental imagery to create a spiritual protector. This protector must be strong and powerful enough to keep you safe. Some survivors report having a fierce animal such as a bear, lion, tiger, or a room-sized rat appear. Some will image someone like the Incredible Hulk, a grandparent, a parent who they believed would have wanted to protect them under different circumstances, or their therapist. When the protector is perceived to be a person, the survivor must image this person with supernatural power and superhuman strengths and abilities. This is critical because real people have not been able to provide protection from abuse in the past. Clients must draw from a guaranteed source of power if they are to go back into that horrible past experience. There is an obvious transition from panic to tranquility once your frightening memory has been rescripted with a safe outcome.

Once in a while a survivor starts out with an ineffective protector. This is simply a reflection of learned despair—the belief that nothing can help. To find a workable protector, you simply go back into the memory and rescript it. The protector need not be the same entity each time. It may vary from situation to situation. The only requirement is that it is effective in keeping you safe. The protector you begin with may not be sufficient for dealing with later memories.

One woman I worked with began by using her childhood dog as her protector while dealing with memories of being sexually abused by her father; however, the next time she used her dog as her protector, she saw her father beating the it, an event that had really happened. When I suggested she find a more effective protector for both herself and the dog, she saw a huge rat which was warm and protective toward herself and her dog, but was fierce and powerful with her abuser.

There were times when I would have to remind this woman that her protector could do anything required to insure her safety. Once, when she was experiencing a memory of being tied and unable to break free from the leather cuffs on her wrists and ankles, I reminded her that her protector could help. She envisioned the rat miraculously making her wrists and ankles small enough to allow her to slip out of her bondage. Sometimes this woman would have her protector take her to a safe house where she could stand in the shower and cleanse the abuse from her body. Other times the protector would escort her to a playground across the street from her grandmother's house, a place where she had felt safe as a child.

Using Your Spiritual Protector

Having a spiritual protector allows us to believe that we never have to be alone with our abuse memories and we never have to relive them in the same way we experienced them as children. We have the power and ability to see our memories with new, positive, and safe endings.

It's important to understand that there are times when we must go back into the past to understand it and put the pieces together so we can feel whole and complete as integrated people. It's just as important to know that we don't have to constantly relive our traumatic experiences with the same negative outcomes. Once we have felt and released the blocked emotions and safely removed ourselves from the danger, we are free to revisit our experiences so we can learn.

I urge you to go back with your protector, but avoid submerging yourself into the memory again and again. Stand back with your protector as an observer. Witness what happened from a safe distance so you can gather data without subjecting yourself to reliving the trauma. When my mind flashes back to one of my worst memories, I now automatically see the situation with a new ending. I have a clear picture of a beautiful, powerful tiger rescuing me from the abuse. I no longer have to remember to do this with memories I have revisited. I have rewritten the story within my mind and now see it in a safe way. My body doesn't have to constantly fight off shock reactions because I'm not subjecting my system to the same old abuse. I have given my mind and body a corrective experience which they have integrated as a new part of me.

The traumatic episodes I went through were horrible and I was exposed to the abuse without any protector to take care of me. What I have done as an adult is devise a way to be in charge of my mind, body, and past by drawing from my spiritual being through use of a spiritual protector. I am in charge of deciding to never be alone and unprotected in my past. The mentally imaged protector spiritually parents and protects the frightened little child in me. It's a wonderful energizing feeling to know I'm able to provide myself with the protection I need from my past. By discarding the helpless victim style of relating to the past, I now feel my own source of strength and power. I am no longer powerless over my past, and neither are you.

This protector concept can be expanded upon and used in other helpful ways. Sometimes we spend so much of our lives thinking about awful things that we develop a habit of keeping our minds occupied with misery. If you have a memory that keeps coming back to you, ask yourself, "Is there anything more I can learn from this?" If the answer is yes, then revisit the memory from a distance with your protector and see what there is to see in order to gain needed insights. If the answer is no, then you may be playing out those old memories out of habit because you're not accustomed to thinking about pleasant things. If your family of origin focused on the negative and did not know how to get and tolerate pleasure and joy, you are likely to be stuck in these same thought processes. You may need to consciously choose to think pleasant thoughts.

When my daughter was five years old, she had a few scary dreams after watching a television show. She woke up from these dreams and was unable to go back to sleep. When my husband and I encouraged her to think of something pleasant, she envisioned herself being held in the arms of a beautiful, loving angel, and she was easily able to fall asleep. She has since used this same image whenever she is feeling distressed.

The mind wants to be busy with something, so if we want to get rid of a bothersome thought or image, it is more effective to replace it with something positive than to try to block it out. The more we practice thinking about pleasant scenes, with or without our spiritual protector, the easier it is to conjure up something positive when we want to replace something negative. Our mental images don't have to be complicated. In fact, the simpler they are, the more likely they will work.

Let me give you some examples of simple, pleasant images. I love the face I see in a colorful, velvety pansy, so it's always pleasant for me to create the picture of a pansy or a garden full of pansies. If I'm feeling uncomfortably hot, I allow myself to see a large, frosted glass of lemonade, or I see myself running and jumping into a swimming pool. If I want an image of coolness that is more spiritual, I see myself standing under the gentle spray of a secluded, sunlit waterfall. If I'm feeling lonely, I see myself walking and talking with a friend, my husband, or my daughter. If I feel like giving, I picture myself holding my daughter while I read her a story. Be creative while discovering what positive images are most effective for you. Just as you were trained as a child to see the world as frightening and threatening, you now have the power as a competent adult to train yourself to be open to the beauty and wonder of life.

Mental Imagery Exercises

*Think of a mildly scary memory—just scary enough that you feel some fear. Close your eyes and feel the fear. Be aware of your rapid breathing and heartbeat as well as your desire to flee. Bring your protector into the scary memory and have it do whatever you need to get you out of the situation and help you feel safe. For example, if you see yourself as a young child being hassled by a bully, then see your protector sending that bully away from you. Now see your protector removing you from the dangerous situation and placing you in a safe situation. Once you have allowed your protector to bring you to safety, notice how your breathing, heart rate, and overall fear level change.

*If you have difficulty thinking of nice memories or focusing on current or future goals, create a pleasant scene in which your protector provides you with whatever it is you are needing at the time. If you're feeling scared and unsafe, imagine your protector surrounding you protectively. If you're feeling unloved and empty, imagine your protector holding you in a warm and tender manner, giving you the nurturing you need and deserve. If you need to experience a sense of playful joy, see your protector playing with you while swimming, swinging, or playing catch.

6

Releasing and Integrating Emotions

It's very important not to be alone when you are processing memories. This would repeat the neglect that took place both during and after the abuse. There likely wasn't anybody there at that time to protect, to comfort, and help you process your way through the trauma. You were terribly alone, left in isolation to experience and analyze everything by yourself. This is what led you to making inaccurate interpretations, assumptions, and conclusions as to the meaning of, and responsibility for, the abuse.

When you are an adult reliving the terrible feelings of your childhood traumas, you need a therapist or other qualified adult with you. That person can tell you that you are safe, that you are reliving a bad memory. That person can help you understand that you did not make your parents do bad things to you. They did what they did by their own choice. This person can help you remember what the healthy portion of you already understands, that children can't make adults sexually abuse them, but adults can easily make children believe that they caused it to happen.

When you are reliving a memory, you return to that little child state, with your little child thinking. What you need is someone to speak to the rational, adult part of you to help you understand how that little child put the pieces together. As a little child, you did the best you could, but you got it wrong when you took the blame. You were unable to realize this at the time of the abuse; you ended up believing your abuser. It is precisely those lies which have to be confronted and challenged by another adult mind. Having this other person there to help sort out the truth makes it possible to understand what happened in a way far different from how you understood it as a child.

The best thing your therapist can do for you is to sit by you, close enough for you to be able to reach out and touch him or her if you want someone to hang on to. You need your therapist to listen and to orient you to reality by reminding you that it is a bad memory and that it isn't happening right now. After you have experienced the memory and released the emotion, you are ready to open your eyes and process both what you felt and what you understand from the experience.

After reliving a memory, you are likely to feel overwhelmed by shame. One of the functions of your therapist is to help eradicate the shame by helping you understand that you are not a bad person. You were confused as a result of being lied to, and consequently came to believe you were a bad person. Upon seeing and feeling the memory, the childhood interpretations become very clear, they can be stated openly, and they can be challenged and corrected. You can expect to be surprised by what you thought as a child. What you say about these interpretations will feel quite absurd on one level, yet absolutely real on another. Your adult mind knows the interpretations are ridiculous, but your child mind believes them wholeheartedly.

Emotion as Energy

Experiencing and processing memories is all about dealing with emotions. I visualize emotions by seeing them as an energy form that flows along our internal electrical system and is regulated by our breathing patterns. Emotions are a normal physiological reaction to thoughts. There are four basic emotions: anger, sadness, joy, and fear. According to the theories of bioenergetics, each of these basic emotions has its own physiological pathway.

Anger

Anger typically moves up the back of the body along the spine, over the top of the head and out through the eyes and mouth. It also travels down the arms and out through the hands. This tendency of anger to move along the back side of the body is reflected in such expressions as *pain in the neck* or *pain in the butt*. This is why, when we become very angry with someone, we instinctively tighten our fists in response to the anger moving through our arms and hands. Also, if you closely monitor your body when you are angry, you are likely to sense a surge of energy coming through your eyes and to feel your jaw tightening prior to making any angry verbal statements. This pattern of build-up and natural discharge within the body is consistent for all emotions. As with other feelings, the degree of anger we feel varies. We may feel mild anger, which we might describe as irritation or annoyance, or we might feel rage, a form of anger that we feel as blinding or out of control.

Once you experience a thought that makes you angry, you will have body energy that needs to be released. Altering thoughts to perceive the situation differently may help avoid additional anger, but the original energy still needs to be released. If the energy is relatively small, simply saying you are angry may be enough to do the job. If it is a large amount, you may need a more complete release.

Many of us have tremendous anger related to our abuse, and this anger is extremely frightening. We seem to have this intuitive fear that touching our anger will lead to a loss of control and might create the same type of damage we witnessed within our families of origin. This fear causes us to keep a tight lid on our anger, thereby creating tension headaches as well as a mass of painful knots throughout our upper back muscles.

The trick to releasing anger in a healthy, productive fashion involves finding the proper amount of containment so it comes out in a safe, useful manner. It is not okay to splatter anger everywhere. Verbally abusing others, screaming at people, and breaking things are not necessary to the release of anger, nor are they appropriate and acceptable actions. *The fact that you were abused doesn't give you the right to abuse others.*

When you're dealing with just a little anger, simply saying how you are feeling, writing your feelings in a journal, tightening and squeezing a fist while perhaps making a grunting sound or sighing, or pounding a fist down once on a soft surface are all potentially effective ways of allowing an outlet for the energy. It is vital to think about the reasons for your anger while you are releasing it from your body. There should be an integrated experience of knowing you are angry, knowing why you are angry, and then releasing the anger. This ensures the coordination of mind, emotion, and body in the search for resolution.

Other techniques are available for dealing with more intense feelings of anger. Playing racquetball or hitting a tennis ball against a wall may be helpful. Since standing up while angry can cause some people to feel at risk of losing control, I've outlined some anger releasing exercises that involve lying on your bed or kneeling on the floor. These can be found at the end of the chapter.

Releasing Anger. In addition to the methods I've already described, there are many ways to release anger. As long as you remember that the anger energy wants to release along the backside through the arms, eyes, and legs, you can find your own creative outlets. Speed walking, jogging, soccer, pulling out weeds by the roots, swimming, and weightlifting are some activities which others find effective for safely releasing anger. Moving the anger out through an active body allows us to discover our inner power and sense of control. It's difficult to feel like a victim when we are directing the movement of our anger through our moving bodies. The constructive movement and release of exercise eases our thoughts out of the victim pattern as we establish control over emotional expression.

Sadness

Sadness is a tender emotion that comes up the front of the body, through the throat into the face, and up to the eyes. We release sadness through crying.

The two most common ways of blocking the flow of sadness energy are to avoid breathing so the diaphragm muscle constricts, thereby holding the sadness in the gut, and to constrict the throat muscles. You have used this second technique for blocking sadness whenever you have felt a thick lump in the throat while holding back tears. When we do this consistently a chronic, painful ache develops in our throats and our throat muscles will be very tight to the touch. Breathing is the key to expressing sadness through crying. Deep breathing opens the diaphragm, allowing the throat muscles to relax away the lump in the throat. The sad energy is then free to travel up the front side of the body and out through the eyes.

Peeling onions can help to open up the tear ducts if they are fairly constricted. Sad songs or movies can help trigger sadness in you. You might find yourself attracted to sad books, movies, songs, or newspaper articles. These outlets help you connect to the sadness associated with your own abuse.

Expressing Sadness. Other activites also have the potential to trigger sadness. Many women are able to experience deep sobbing after their bodies open for a sexual orgasm. Watching parents with their children at a neighborhood mall or park can precipitate feelings of sadness, either through identification with the children being abused or by seeing them receive the love and nurturing we didn't get. It is important to give ourselves permission to use anything which taps into our sadness. Connect with people who are supportive when you cry, or take time alone if the presence of others seems to hinder you.

Sadness is frequently hidden behind anger,

and vice versa. It is not unusual for someone to break into deep sobbing after releasing anger. Some of us are more comfortable with sadness than with anger, so we might start to cry immediately upon feeling angry. This may well be helpless despair coming up as we try to assert ourselves with our anger. If this happens to you, it is very important that you push on ahead and continue with the anger work even though you are crying and wanting to stop. If you move forward, the anger will strengthen you, pull you out of the despair, and help you connect with your deep, grieving sadness. Then allow yourself to curl up and sob like a baby while holding on to someone. If no one is available, hold on a soft blanket, stuffed animal, or pillow for nurturance as you grieve out your sadness. Bringing in a nurturing protector at this point through use of mental imagery can feel very supportive and healing.

Joy

We experience joy primarily on the front side of the body, running up and down the full length of the torso. Joy can be experienced as sexual energy in the genital region, or higher in the body, completely separate from sexual energy. Joy can be that funny feeling in the stomach that comes with swinging on a swing or going over and down a hill while riding in a fast-moving car. Dancing, singing, smiling, and jumping are all outlets for the feeling of joy. Sometimes the energy of joy is also released through tears.

We may tend to block or hold in joy if we were shamed by others during childhood. Many of us were instructed in a shaming way to "settle down" when we were merely happy and moving to release our joy. Kids love to jump, sing, and dance out their joy. Unfortunately, an emotionally constricted family will not tolerate too much of anything, whether it is happiness, sadness, anger, or fear.

Another powerful reason why incest survivors frequently hold in joy is a common belief that letting go of joy will unleash all the internal pain as well. Sometimes the constriction stems from a belief that we do not deserve to feel good, but often it results from an attempt to avoid our pain.

Joy is held in by breathing very shallowly and

by frequently holding our breath. Opening up our breathing allows the energy of joy to move through the body. This process can be frightening for many of us because the energy can drop down into the pelvic area where sexual feelings are experienced. This may trigger unwanted memories of abuse, or shameful feelings as a result of having experienced sexual feelings during the incest.

Showing Joy. As with sadness, joy moves up the front side of the body as we open up our breathing. One way to train ourselves to open up our breathing is by singing out while we're driving. You don't need a good voice in order to feel joy from singing, the movement of breath creates this feeling. Dancing will also open up breathing. As our rigid muscular constriction begins to loosen and our fear becomes less intense, the feeling of joy will flow more and more naturally.

How long has it been since you've gone swimming, ice skating, or sliding down a snowy hill? The rides at a state fair or carnival can offer an opportunity to open breathing and connect with joy. Buy or borrow a bicycle and coast down a big hill. All these activities have the potential to put us in touch with our joy and our sense of personal power.

Take into account how naturally introverted or extroverted you are and find activities that fit. Don't try to find joy at a large, loud party if you're an introvert. Don't go to a movie alone if you're an extrovert, just because you've heard this would be good for you. We shouldn't ever have to apologize for or try to change our basic nature; that is not the path to joy. We're just fine the way we are.

Fear

We typically feel fear in the pit of the stomach. It can move along the front side of the body or it can travel along the spine. When I ask clients what happens in their bodies when they are scared, the most common response is that they tighten up. Actually, the stiffening is an attempt to avoid feeling the fear. We release fear through trembling or shaking. Think about a child who has not yet learned to repress fear and who is giving a first book report in front of the class. Trembling legs and hands may cause feelings of shame, so the child will keep the breath shallow while tightening the body in an effort to control the fear.

Fear will actually pass more quickly if you allow the energy to be released through trembling, as long as you are now in a safe situation. If you remain in a frightening situation, you will continue to experience thoughts indicating you are not safe, thereby generating new fear. Once your thoughts can be consistent with being safe, the terror of fear will pass much more quickly if you take some slow, deep breaths and give your body a chance to shake out the fear.

Coping With Fear. Coping with fear requires us to become comfortable with trembling so the body can have its release. When small children are very frightened, they feel safe when their bodies tremble while someone provides a sense of containment by holding them. If you are going through a particularly difficult time because you are experiencing a lot of fear from childhood abuse, you may find comfort in having a caring, nurturing person hold you, or in wrapping yourself tightly in a blanket.

Emotion-Releasing Exercises

*Lie on a bed with your eyes open (so the energy has an outlet for discharge) and, alternating your fully extended arms, pound the mattress forcefully. Bring your legs up and drop them onto the mattress. In other words, have a safe, contained temper tantrum. You can also do this exercise while lying on your stomach, but be certain you place a pillow under your abdomen to give your lower back necessary support.

*A variation on this same approach involves using an old tennis racquet to hit against a pile of pillows or a mattress while you are kneeling on the floor. If you should use this technique, it is important to do it properly to avoid jamming the energy in your neck and spraining a muscle. Let your head and neck follow through at the same level as your arms. Avoid keeping your head up and extended while your arms come down, as this will generate the energy jam noted above. Kneel with your legs apart to give you a solid base of support. Keep your eyes open at all times when you are releasing anger or you will get a splitting headache. If you should forget to open your eyes and then get a headache, simply open them and hit a few more times. This should be sufficient to allow the energy to release. Allow words and sound to come out as you are hitting. Stomping your feet as part of the exercise may feel good, especially if your anger is coming from a repressed and dominated toddler within you who was never allowed to say no.

*An effective way of relaxing your throat muscles and correcting the blockage that occurs when we hold back tears is to take a slow, deep breath through the nose and down into the abdomen. Then fill the chest so the diaphragm can expand and follow by exhaling through the mouth. You may also need to open your mouth, tilt your head back slightly, and suck in air to open your throat.

*One way of getting used to the sensation of joy in a nonthreatening way is to go to a neighborhood playground and do some slow swinging. It is important to avoid pushing yourself into feelings of fear. Swing slowly and work on staying in your body while you do this. Gradually build up your tolerance for joy by adding a little more height to your swinging.

*Put yourself into a controlled situation that will create a small amount of fear. Looking over a tall building or bridge, swinging a little too high, pedalling a little too fast down a hill, or imagining a scary situation are ways to connect with the feeling of fear. Come to know your body's reaction to fear by constricting against it and then letting it go.

7

Managing Shame

Identifying the presence of shame is a crucial first step in the process of reducing, in frequency and duration, when and how we experience it. Shame-based people often fail to see the extent to which they are affected. Shame is triggered by many basic activities of daily life. When we resist calling the doctor's office to question a bill because we don't want to be a burden, or when we ask our spouse to pick up our prescription at the pharmacy because it would feel uncomfortable to do so personally, we are feeling shame.

You can learn to recognize your shame by paying attention to how you present yourself physically. When you sit or stand in a slouched position with your head hanging or when you avoid eye contact by staring at the floor, you are feeling shame. Use your insight about shame as a way to begin correcting it. Remind yourself that nothing is wrong with you. Unhealthy, dysfunctional, family members made you feel deficient because they were incapable of validating your developmentally appropriate needs and feelings. An ill-prepared mother may have felt you were the cause of her problems and, as a result of this misperception, may have let you know she felt burdened by having you around.

Stop yourself during these shame attacks and say something like, "Oh, I'm feeling that old shame again. I'm feeling worthless because I was taught to feel that way about myself. It's all a lie. I'm just fine the way I am." Call on your ideal family through the mental imagery exercise described below. Hear what these people have to say about your situation and let them confirm that your real family lied to you about your worth as a person.

You can also work directly with the body to correct shame by adopting a new posture. Force yourself to straighten your body and look up. Establish and maintain eye contact with others.

Walk purposefully and without hesitation.

Getting a handle on or reducing our shame may seem like a lot of work at first, but it becomes easier with practice. You will gradually internalize this new way of thinking and posturing and you will no longer have to constantly correct yourself. Accept the fact that it is appropriate for people to comment if you are being offensive, but if they challenge your total worth as a human being, their comments are a reflection of where they are with themselves and have nothing to do with you.

Cleansing Original Shame

I would like to lead you through another mental imagery exercise which has proven useful for many people who are identifying and correcting shame. This exercise is intended for those who are shame-based about all of themselves—they feel rotten to the core. This exercise requires more detailed instruction than some of the others we've suggested; therefore, we're presenting it within the text instead of at chapter end. Another exercise that focuses on issue-specific shame-based behavior will be presented at chapter end.

This exercise will help you regress to earlier ages, to help determine the approximate time when shame became established within you. The point at which the shame took root is also the point at which it is most effectively corrected.

You may connect with the feeling of shame during this exercise in several ways. When you ask yourself if you had the shame at a particular age, you may only hear yourself saying yes, or you may see yourself actually experiencing the shame with your head hanging down. You may feel the shame within your body along with the need to cry—you may even start to cry. All these reactions are appropriate indicators of shame at a particular age.

I will go through the exercise by working back all the way to the womb and then outline the corrective part of the process for you. If you discover that the time of onset of your shame is after you were in the womb, stop the regression at that point and apply the corrective part of the exercise. If your childhood experience was similar to that of most of the people I have worked with, you will find that you must regress all the way back to the beginning to identify the origin of your shame-based identity. Once again, you may tape the following instructions for yourself if you wish. It may make the exercise easier to follow.

Begin by sitting back in a comfortable position with your eyes gently closed. Breathe deeply and slowly, inhaling through your nose and exhaling through your mouth.

When you feel ready, picture yourself at age twenty-five and ask yourself if you had that shameful unworthy feeling then. (If you are not yet twenty-five, start with the closest age younger than you which is divisible by five and modify the regressing accordingly.) Assuming you were shame-based at age twenty-five, regress to twenty and repeat the question about the presence of shame. Should you conclude the shame was not present at any point in this regression exercise, you will have established a five year range within which this feeling became a part of who you are. You can then move up one year at a time within this range until you pinpoint the exact time it became a part of you.

If you should reach age five in this process and

still feel the presence of the shame, move next to age two. You may not be able to get a clear visual image of yourself at this age, but you will be able to know whether you were shame-based then. Your body will remember the sensation. Move next to age one and then go to six months. It is important that you take your time and learn what this feeling and your experiences were like at these different ages. Don't challenge the validity of what you observe; simply note your observations and let yourself feel whatever emotions surface.

Take yourself back to the time of your birth and determine whether shame is present. If it is, allow yourself to move back into the womb. Ask about the presence of shame while you are in the womb. Also, ask how it feels in there. Is it calm and peaceful, or do you sense a great deal of tension? Do you experience it to be a clean pure environment, or does it seem cloudy and toxic? How does your mother feel about having you in there? See her face. Is she smiling down at you in a pleased way, or does she look and feel angry, frustrated, burdened, or fearful? How about your father? How does he seem to feel about you being in the womb preparing to enter the world?

If you sense a negative environment in the womb, ask yourself about the shame. Who do you believe is responsible for this bad feeling in your mother and in the womb? Even though it may not appear to be very rational, does it somehow feel as though you're the cause for your mother's unhappiness? Do you have the sense that just by showing up you are the burden and the problem? Do you feel unwanted because there is something defective or bad about you? Pay particular attention to the phrase or phrases that come to you to describe how you experience the rejection and abandonment. Also, listen to how you conclude that it's your supposed unworthiness or defectiveness that triggered the rejection and abandonment. As you do this, keep your breathing open so you are able to release any emotion that comes to the surface.

Now let yourself be born to your parents and see if there are new insights about the origin of your negative, shaming attitudes. Get a sense about how your parents feel about you being the sex you are. Do they want to cuddle and feed you? Do they delight in the beauty of your expression? Or are they disappointed with your sex and appearance? Do they withdraw in response to their sense of being burdened by your needs? When you feel finished with this portion of the exercise, it's time to move forward into the corrective part of the process so you can gain a new, healthier perspective on your worth and inherent beauty.

While remembering the image of yourself within your family as you just experienced it, allow yourself to be lifted out of that picture and to come down into a new, ideal mother's womb with an ideal father affectionately standing by. Imagine this is a couple absolutely ready to have a child. They have planned you, and they are eagerly awaiting your arrival. Your mother is calmly enjoying your start within her body, and she is looking forward to your birth.

See these people having a warm, intimate, and committed relationship with each other. It's a relationship established by two people who love themselves and feel complete outside their marriage, but who chose marriage to each other because it was a desirable enriching addition to life. They have already been nurtured and emotionally filled up. They don't *need* a child to provide meaning to empty, troubled lives. They *want* a child so they can enjoy the rich experience of parenting. They have a need as well as the capacity to give, and they believe this is the best time to do so by having a child.

Spend some time in your new womb, and, when you're ready, see yourself being received by these loving parents at your birth. If you wish, also see siblings waiting excitedly for you. See them as being without any need to compete with you for attention because they know there is plenty of love to go around.

Ask how you would have felt about yourself while going through life as a member of this ideal family. Would you feel shame about your existence or your needs? Or would you feel accepted and worthy simply for being who you are? See yourself going through some of the difficult ages of your life while in this new family. Experience fully how differently you would have been treated and, as a result, how differently you would have felt about yourself. Allow yourself to see that it wasn't you who was the problem; it was that you had the misfortune to enter a family which was ill-prepared to deal with your normal developmental needs.

Let your emotions surface and release them as you experience the ideal family in contrast to the real family. Finish the corrective portion of the exercise by bringing yourself up to your current age after you have traveled through life with your ideal family. When you have reached the present moment, let your eyes gradually open and orient yourself. This concludes this shame exercise.

If you find it difficult to image your ideal parents giving you positive messages, substitute any person you believe is a healthy affirming individual. This person can be someone you know personally, an author of a book you've read, a speaker you've heard, or someone else. You can use anyone who will provide a more affirming message than the one you received within your family of origin.

Single-Issue Shame

Sometimes shame is issue-specific. We can

feel shame around such things as sexuality, sadness, or anger without necessarily feeling worthless. Ask yourself how your family dealt with the issue around which you feel shameful. If your shame is issue-specific rather than all-encompassing, you can modify the exercise described above and use it to help bring about healing.

Mental Imagery Exercise

*See yourself at various ages being sad or joyful or in need of comforting and pay attention to the reactions of others in your family. This will help you understand how you took in shame about that particular emotion or need. Use the regression technique until you reach the point where you are shame-free, and then move forward until you establish the age and circumstances that surround the development of your shame. Take some time picturing yourself in the negative experience until you've learned from it and felt within it. Now give yourself an ideal family which permits you to receive correct and supportive messages about what happened, or which offers permission and validation about your needs and emotions.

8

Protecting Your Boundaries

I think of people's emotional and physical pain as energy forms. I believe it is possible to direct such energy forms with the mind. We have the ability to redirect undesirable energy forms away from us and to know whether a problem belongs to us or someone else. In this chapter I'll offer some mental imagery exercises which can be effective in protecting your boundaries.

In many cases we were overly sensitive and highly perceptive children who knew what was going on in our families and were disturbed by it. We often tried to correct what was going on by taking care of everyone. Unfortunately, this care-taking business was a thankless job. Not only did other family members fail to appreciate our efforts, they generally resented our attempts to correct the situation. They told us we were the problem. Even worse, we were risking emotional and physical burnout from carrying such a load for the family. As adults now, it's critical to learn the skill of avoiding taking on the pains and problems of others. We are quite capable of ridding ourselves of this oppressive caretaking burden.

Developing and Maintaining Boundaries

The glass body imagery exercise described at the end of this chapter can be an effective way to learn about and develop boundaries. It helps us find clarity about what belongs to us and what belongs to others. It allows us to focus on being responsible for ourselves without taking on other people's feelings and problems.

Perform the glass body exercise each morning. I find it's an excellent way to start the day, especially those days when I'm working with clients or scheduled to be in a large crowd. I also use this technique whenever I feel myself starting to take on someone's feelings. I imagine the glass body and instantly release all emotions which don't belong to me. I say to myself, "This isn't my sadness (or anger or fear)." Then I direct the emotions to pass through the glass body.

Whenever you want to cry in response to someone sharing their sadness with you, ask yourself if the other person's feeling has triggered some of your own unfinished sadness. If it has, then decide if this is the most desirable and appropriate time to deal with your sadness. If you decide it isn't, tell yourself you will deal with these feelings later.

It's important to realize that we can't handle other people's feelings for them. We can take on another's feelings for the moment, thereby diffusing them, but this will have the effect of blocking emotional release and resolution for the other person. Those unresolved feelings will only surface again later, so we might as well send them back to the owner right now so healing can begin. I frequently sit with clients who want to cry but are blocking their feelings. I often find myself wanting to cry in response to their emotion. As soon as I send their sadness back to them by way of the glass body image, I no longer feel sad. Generally, the client begins to cry at this point.

Many clients have told me they get angry and resentful whenever their partner takes on the emotion they are expressing. This anger stems from having an important boundary violated. They know at some level that they are entitled to have their own feelings and that they should be allowed to express them while their partner simply listens supportively. Letting another person do our feeling for us is another way we play out the victim role.

No matter how pure the intentions, emotional merging contaminates both parties in a relationship. It can easily lead to controlling rather than helping. Letting go of whatever belongs to someone else helps us move away from controlling ways. Use the glass body exercise to practice defining and staying within your boundaries. We clean up important relationships when we purge ourselves of feelings that properly belong to another.

Pain into Dust is another exercise I explain at the end of the chapter, but I encourage you to trust yourself and experiment with other images until you discover one which is best for you.

Some authors recommend protecting yourself from others' feelings and negativity by putting up a mental shield in front of you or by surrounding yourself with white light. It has been my experience that these techniques require excessive energy by requiring you to be constantly on guard and by forcing you to create something to hold off the undesired. The glass body image requires less energy because it uses the concept of least resistance. Rather than being on guard at all times and actively resisting something, you prevent merging by letting go.

Letting Go of Negative Energy

Have you ever noticed how you can start out feeling fine only to end up in a lousy mood after being around someone who is awash in negative energy? There are many ways to conquer the negative. My husband taught our daughter a little trick to use whenever someone is bugging her with negative energy. He taught her to image the offending party becoming very small, perhaps an inch or less. Then she can pick up the person, drop him or her into a garbage can, and close the lid. After stopping the flow of negative energy, she can then clean out any that might have already contaminated her.

When you are extremely agitated by a negative situation, you can bring it under control by seeing a picture of it, imaging a plug at the bottom of the picture, pulling the plug so the negative energy can drain away, and seeing this energy flow out and turn into dust. Once the energy has drained away from the picture, put the plug back in. This can give you a sense of control as well as make you more objective about dealing with the situation. It is another way of saying, "I refuse to let you win by allowing you to get to me."

This is not to suggest that we deny our emotions, but it isn't helpful to be contaminated by the negative energy of others. Should you discover you are infected, there are some basic steps you can take to get yourself to a more positive place. Once again, be creative and experiment until you find a technique which is truly effective for you.

Mental Imagery Exercises

*The first imagery exercise is called the Glass Body. Sit back in a relaxed comfortable position with your eyes gently closed. Start by doing the grounding exercise to ensure you are present in your body. Now see yourself sitting exactly as you are. See a completely glass image of yourself facing you. Make certain the entire image is glass, including your head. Now see the image turning around and sitting down into you so you become the glass body. Once you have imaged yourself being as a glass body, say to yourself, "I am a glass body. Everything that is not mine, such as other people's emotions, physical pain, and problems, will pass through me like sunshine through a pane of glass. Whatever is mine I will keep and be responsible for. But whatever is not mine will pass right through me." As you say this, visualize and sense sunshine passing through you.

*When my daughter was about five, she told me she felt the pain of other people when she saw them get hurt. If someone fell down and skinned a leg, her leg began to hurt in the same place. I explained that the pain wasn't really her pain, and it didn't help her or the other person if she felt it as well. She readily agreed with me. I suggested she send the pain back to where it belonged, since it wasn't hers. She didn't like the idea of having someone else hurt, so she decided to turn the pain into dust. She has used this technique many times over the years and it continues to be effective. She has also learned to use this approach for other people's emotions as well as their physical pain.

*Sit comfortably with your hands touching the arms of the chair and your feet resting flat on the floor. It is important that your hands be placed on the chair and not on your body. With your eyes open or closed depending upon your personal preference, image and experience all the undesirable energy draining out of your feet and hands and flowing into the floor and chair. Continue to do this until you feel thoroughly grounded, in a good mood, and completely cleansed of all negative energy. Some people find it helpful to breathe in slow deep breaths and watch the breath fill up their own internal space as the negative energy drains away. Others like to draw from a spiritual place by seeing white light come in through the crown of the head and gradually filter down, filling them up as the undesirable energy is emptied out.

9

That Deep Empty Feeling

Most of the incest survivors I have worked with try to hide from the world because of their intense and overwhelming sense of shame. At the same time, they dread coming in contact with that empty lonely feeling which seems to permeate their very core. Eventually they own up to feeling empty in a manner that sounds like a confession. Their need to confess is rooted in the shame-based perception that the loneliness comes from not having friends, and that this absence of friends is a direct consequence of their fundamental deficiencies as human beings.

We experience this empty feeling when we have not had positive bonding interactions with significant others. Incest survivors come from dysfunctional families, typically headed by at least one and perhaps two parents who never adequately bonded or filled up emotionally themselves. We had no healthy bonding experiences. Bonding is essential for the development of a complete whole sense of self. Bonding also gives us the skills required to connect with others in healthy relationships.

We are never too old to learn how to bond with others. You don't have to go through the rest of your life believing there is an empty hole inside that can never be filled. Your therapist, a friend, a spouse, or a grandparent could serve as your first significant bonding partner. The identity of the person isn't important, but it is critical that he or she be someone whose heart is open to you. He or she must also have loving and accepting attitudes about you as a person. You may find yourself connecting to and receiving validation from several people at the same time.

I frequently record a personalized relaxation exercise for my clients and encourage them to use it when they feel lonely. I believe they will benefit from the relaxation and mental imagery guidance, but I also believe having the exercise recorded in my voice serves to enhance the bonding process. Adults who had good bonding relationships with their parents will often ask themselves what their parents might say or do in a particular situation. There is no reason why you can't find substitute parents now if they weren't available to you when you were a child. Therapists can certainly fill the role for a while.

The more you are able to carry within you the good words and feelings received from interacting with others, the more you are bonding. The more you take in from others, the more you will be able to hear your own adult mind comforting and validating the uncertain child within you. This is how you learn to fill in that empty ache you have been carrying for so long.

We can benefit from hugging ourselves, but not until we experience what it feels like to be hugged by another person. A mental image of being held by God or a guardian angel will only work if our skin and soul know what it feels like in real life. Even though we can receive great comfort from mental images, they will never completely replace our need for physical and emotional connection with real people. We are not designed to live alone and be totally self-sufficient. There will, of course, be individual differences in how and how much we want to connect with others, but everyone needs relationships to avoid feeling empty. The process of establishing connections with other human beings helps us heal the damage inflicted by incest.

Mental Imagery Exercises

*It helps when you are just learning to fill in the gaps to bring your special person or persons along with you as you go about your daily life. I mean this in a symbolic sense. In your mind, let them talk to you and be supportive. If you have done something well, imagine that special person or persons smiling at you with pride and respect. Hear them saying the validating praising words you need to hear. If you have made a mistake, let yourself hear their constant acceptance of you as a human being.

*If you are lonely, talk to your bonding partner in your mind and share what you are going through. You can also write a letter to him or her. Make certain the talking flows not only from you to your partner but also the other way. Listen to the reactions and responses. Remember that children who are in the process of defining themselves need responses from others so they can learn to rely on themselves for their own self-definition.

*If you're feeling scared when alone or when you are about to do something frightening, imagine your special person being with you to offer whatever support you need. I remember going for a job interview long ago when I still had not completely accepted that the outcome of an interview is not the final word on how worthy I am as a human being. To help me get through this situation I imagined my husband and therapist sitting on my shoulders. They helped me feel grounded, and they were also ready to kick anybody who dared say something mean to me. It was a powerful game that served to take the intensity out of the interview as well as give me the support I needed at the time.

10

Recovering

To make any positive change we must develop a constructive attitude. As long as we think and act like victims, nothing of substance will change. Understanding that our victim thinking, feeling, and behavior can be replaced by healthy thinking, feeling, and behavior is the first step toward healing the splits within us. This understanding gives us the strength to initiate positive change in other areas of our lives.

Like other humans, we have our rough edges and our blind spots, but we are also children of God or Good and therefore worthy and deserving of all that is good. It is true we were victimized as children in ways nobody should have to suffer, but it is also true that we have opportunities as adults to share in all that is wonderful and joyous.

As adults, it is within our power and it is our right to create the proper conditions so that we no longer think, feel, and behave as victims. We are responsible for our happiness, contentment, and overall mental, emotional, physical, and spiritual health. Victims shirk responsibility for living by hiding behind the seductive illusion that others are responsible for their happiness and sense of wholeness. We will never reach these important goals unless we make a firm commitment to ourselves that we will do what it takes to bring about positive change. Accepting personal responsibility does not mean we must complete each detail of every step in the recovery process by ourselves. In fact, trying to do it alone will make it less likely that desired changes will actually take place. It is your right and your responsibility to ask for help. We have appropriate boundaries when we acknowledge what we can do ourselves and realize when we need help.

Choosing a Psychotherapist

Choosing and working with a psychotherapist provides an opportunity for developing and expanding your new nonvictim attitude. You have the right to navigate through your recovery journey with the help of a therapist who you perceive to be respectful, caring, and supportive of your healing. You don't have to "make do" with a particular therapist because you've always settled for less than you deserve. You are too important for that.

Remember, therapy dealing with incest and family dysfunction will make you uncomfortable, frightened, and confused, so it is important to work with someone with whom you are compatible. There are many ways to heal, and there are big differences in style among therapists. The best way to determine what is right for you is to sit quietly, go inside yourself, and ask if it feels right as you try out different approaches. If your body remains relaxed, if your gut doesn't squeeze, if a voice inside your head says, "Yes, this will work," you're probably on the right track. Trust yourself because you know what you need. When you can listen to and trust yourself while choosing a therapist, you are starting to break away from your shame and victim thinking.

Stopping the Judgment Merry-Go-Round

We cannot develop a positive constructive attitude unless we grant ourselves a reprieve from the suffocating negativity of self-judgment. Constantly focusing on our actual or perceived mistakes and flaws only stops us from risking change. Whether we compare ourselves unfavorably against past performance, another person, or some unrealistic expectations, this harsh self-judgment will severely limit our opportunities for personal growth. Positive self-judgments can help us evaluate options and set goals. It is freeing to recognize that we have many choices. We can allow ourselves to pursue a course of action knowing that we can decide if some minor midcourse corrections are needed or even stop and choose a different direction.

Perhaps some examples of negative and positive self-judgment will help you understand the difference between these two ways we process information. Consider a woman who has set a goal of losing twenty pounds. She initially lost ten pounds but has recently gained back five. Which of the following responses is closer to how you would feel in this situation? Are negative self-judgments blocking you from moving forward?

Negative self-judgment: I must be really stupid since I can't figure out how to do this right. My friends don't seem to have any problem losing weight. I guess I'm just cut out to be fat and lazy, so what's the use of trying?

Positive self-judgment: I sure felt better before I gained back those five pounds. Since feeling better is important to me, I'm going to make it a priority to lose weight. I'm calling Sheila to see if she wants to join me for walks in the mornings.

Finding Emotional Freedom

Many of us believe we will be well when we no longer feel anything negative. We think healing means never feeling scared, angry, or sad. We draw from our history of limited options and establish this state of nonfeeling as our goal. It is the most we can visualize in terms of coping with life. But mental health means being comfortable with all our emotions. It means suspending judgment of feelings as good or bad and accepting them as human responses arising from living in this world. Once we learn not to fear our emotions, we are free to experience all of life.

We don't need to deny our feelings or allow them to run our lives. When we develop the skill of processing emotions and learn the technique of open complete breathing, we can decide when to release our feelings. We have control over the timing and manner in which we release the emotional energy created by our thoughts.

Sometimes a client says something during the course of a therapy session that makes me sad. This is not the appropriate time and place for me to deal with my pain, as my client isn't paying me to deal with my feelings. I set aside my emotions and come back to them at the end of the day. When I think about what made me sad earlier, I am able to reconnect with the feeling and let that energy be released through my words and tears. This generally takes a few minutes at most and then I return to a happier mood and focus on another activity. When we accept our feelings and deal with them, they aren't overwhelming.

Problems occur when we invest our energy in keeping our feelings repressed.

An Exercise for Feeling

For people who struggle with balancing expression and containment of feelings, I recommend setting aside a certain amount of time each week to focus on the emotional self. This exercise allows deep feelings to surface and frees us from constant emotional intrusion into the activities of living. When sad, angry, or scary thoughts keep intruding into your concentration and interfering with the task at hand, say to yourself, "I have set aside Tuesday from 7:00 p.m. to 8:00 p.m. for this. I'll think about it then." If you're faithful to yourself and follow through on your commitment to come back to these issues, you'll be amazed at how your mind will let up on you at other times. Your mind just wants to know that you will get to the issues and deal with them. If you fail to follow through, those distracting issues will continue to creep into your thoughts.

This approach also works well for controlling nightmares. Our dreams let us know we have something to be faced. Before going to sleep, say to yourself, "I will deal with my issues during my next therapy session. I will not deal with them in my sleep. I need my sleep to be peaceful and calm, so I will be rested and better able to cope during my waking hours."

I have worked with many clients who have thought and talked about such issues as incest and the deaths of loved ones over an extended time without shedding a single tear. When they use this exercise, even though it feels awkward and scary at first, they are able to begin accessing and expressing their deepest feelings in the therapy session. This permits emotional and physical healing to begin, and offers a well-deserved rest for obsessing minds. It represents significant progress toward mending their mind/emotion/body splits.

Set aside time for dealing with feelings. If after doing this exercise you are still too scared to experience the full depth of your feelings, it may be because you were hurt when you showed your feelings openly as a child. Survivors often report being told to stop crying unless they wanted others to think they were crazy. Betty was told to stop crying or she would be locked up in an institution. Perhaps you were advised to stop crying or you would be given "something to cry about." This experience of being invalidated for our feelings produces a terrible fear of releasing emotion, because doing so represents loss of control, exposure to punishment, or even risk of abandonment.

It is also possible that you are too scared to express your feelings as an adult because you are once again in an unsafe environment. It's not okay for you to live with a partner who shames or batters you whenever you display anger, sadness, or fear. It is your responsibility to move to a new, safe environment, one in which you can openly release emotion.

Learning to express and contain emotions in a healthy, balanced manner gives us the freedom to take whatever time we need to deal with our childhood pain. We can get on with the business of daily living while making room for feelings to surface and release as we go along.

Processing Abuse Memories

We need to trust that we are the best source of the truth. This is a time when it is especially important to access your spiritual being and ask, "What do these memory fragments mean? What really happened?" The first response we hear when we ask ourselves for information or answers about incest memory fragments generally comes from our spiritual being. The conflicting voices we hear are typically our defenses or messages we picked up from our parents during childhood. Words or pictures that spontaneously come to us are what we should trust to be the truth. It's too easy to give away our power to our abusers by looking to them for validation. The truth lies within us and is known to our spiritual being.

The worst thing you can do with memory fragments is try to force yourself to remember more. Try to take an easy, letting-go attitude; trust that whatever you need to know from your past will come to you in a form that you'll be able to understand and emotionally handle. Your memories will come together and make sense if you don't push and if you're patient and trusting with your process.

Having a Healthy Body

Many of us feel hopeless, despairing, and impotent about our unhealthy bodies. We wish the situation were different. We assume that our health will not improve, or if it does, it will be the result of something a doctor does for us. When we make a commitment to ourselves to enjoy good physical health, we are breaking away from victim thinking. We recognize that a physician can assist us because of his or her expertise, but we avoid giving the doctor the power and responsibility for something that primarily depends on us.

Use whatever it takes to motivate yourself to begin taking good care of your health. Perhaps not wanting to be a run down, inactive smoker and boozer like your parents, if that is the case, will provide an incentive. Or maybe your spouse or kids push you to quit smoking, begin exercising, start eating and sleeping properly, and schedule regular medical checkups, so initially you do it for them. It's a very loving act to take care of ourselves for someone else, and gradually we discover that we're practicing healthy behaviors with a positive attitude for ourselves. You'll be amazed at how well your body can recover after so much abuse and neglect.

Owning Our Sexuality

It is our right and our responsibility to set appropriate boundaries when it comes to sexual contact with others. We decide when we will have a sexual connection with another person; we must not let someone else decide for us. Sexual intimacy should result from a mutual decision to physically share love between two adults. Sexual intimacy does not exist when we are acting out of a sense of duty, when we are trying to spare another the pain of rejection, or when we are offering a payback.

It is not only important to establish and maintain boundaries concerning sexual contact in general, but also we must come to terms with our beliefs about specific forms of sex. This means understanding and expressing our feelings about various types of sexual contact. Continuous, open communication is the most helpful way of sharing feelings about sex because this allows for the changing of needs and desires over time. Generally, there is a natural ebb and flow to each person's sexuality that needs to be accommodated.

A common belief of incest survivors, rooted in shame, is that enjoyment of sex is unattainable. If we are successful at moving beyond this belief, we are frequently blocked by a combination of anger and futility as our memories of sexual abuse intrude during sexual contact with our present partner. By allowing memories of childhood abuse to intrude into our present life we let the abuse perpetrator continue to violate our boundaries and invade our space. The perpetrator has no right to be there. But we can have power over the timing when it comes to dealing with our abuse memories. Make use of mental imagery and your open breathing skills to help with intrusive abuse memories, sexual self-image, and sexual performance.

When sexual activity triggers abuse memories, you can use the opportunity to process and clean out more memories, or you can set them aside to be dealt with later. If you temporarily set these memories aside or if you've already processed these memories, pull your attention to the here and now. Open up your breathing, come into your body, and let yourself feel the pleasure of loving, sexual contact. Create thoughts and pictures about how you are sharing adult love with your partner. Remind yourself that your partner isn't your abuser, and your abuser's energy is not welcome or even permitted within your space. Send your abuser's negative energy away as you connect with the positive energy of the moment.

It can be helpful to take some time off from sex when we're feeling particularly regressed and vulnerable. Making love when we feel scared is a way of reinstating the incest, and it can make us feel violated. We must take care not to use regression as a way to avoid sex indefinitely. We must eventually take the risk of sexual involvement as competent adults if we are to feel satisfied, whole, and normal. Talking to your partner about what various sexual acts mean to you, and hearing about how your partner relates to these same acts, helps us release distorted, childhood concepts of sex.

We can begin developing a positive sexual self-image in small, quiet ways. Becoming comfortable with our bodies begins in such simple behaviors as taking relaxing baths, using body lotions, and wearing clothes made from soft material. A nonsexual, therapeutic massage is a good way to start becoming more comfortable with touch. Wearing feminine underclothes we women pick out for ourselves is a quiet, personal way to feel sexual. I encourage you to explore and discover your own ways for bringing out and embracing your sexual self.

As you become sexually active again, don't get hung up on sexual performance and orgasms. Initially let yourself take part in gentle sexual touch and gradually add more as your comfort level increases. Start with an affectionate hand on the shoulder or hug in the kitchen as ways of reconnecting and building intimacy. Practice kissing so it's more than a habit; let it have some feeling and meaning when you kiss good night. Practice being in your body during times of holding and fondling before you concern yourself with having an orgasm. You and your partner will benefit from a gradual learning about how to come together through emotional and sexual intimacy. Joy and physical pleasure through sexual activity as an adult is not only possible for you, it's your right.

Exercises for Dealing with Feelings

*Lie alone on your bed and practice open breathing while thinking about whatever it is that is making you feel angry, scared, or sad. Or perhaps you might sit at a desk or table and write about your feelings in a journal. Listening to music can also help you connect with your emotions. I encourage you to experiment with various approaches until you find one that fits.

11

Breaking the Incest Cycle

Incest results from a dysfunctional relationship between a child and an older person who should be in the role of protecting the child. Because of the damage we suffered as children, we are at significant risk as adults to develop unhealthy, disturbed relationships in many areas of our lives. This includes our relationships with self, Higher Power, family of origin members, friends, coworkers and supervisors, spouse, and children. Insuring that the incest cycle is broken requires making changes in some or all of these areas.

Children learn from what we teach them. This includes what we communicate through words, but it also includes what we model for them through our actions. It is important to talk with our children about their rights as human beings and what they can do if their rights are violated, and it is equally important to demonstrate these nonvictim principles through our daily behaviors. Telling our kids they shouldn't allow themselves to be taken advantage of by a manipulative classmate will have little impact if they continually witness us being taken advantage of by our friends, relatives, and coworkers. The identification and correction of dysfunctional relationships are not only key steps in our own personal recovery programs, they are also essential elements of any effort to smash the incest cycle before it contaminates another generation.

Necessary Changes

Incest survivors frequently live in fear that their children will be sexually abused. Those who do not yet have children are often unwilling to give birth or adopt because they are afraid the pain and ugliness they experienced will also torment their children. All too often incest survivors have no concrete understanding of the dynamics which underlie multi-generational incest patterns. They are nevertheless certain that they can't trust themselves to do quality, safe parenting. Since they didn't receive healthy, positive parenting, they think they must be incapable of it. This is victim thinking.

We hear from the media and others that most abusers were abused themselves when they were children. It is easy to misinterpret this piece of information. Saying that most abusers were also abused is not the same as saying that all people who were abused will in turn perpetrate incest. Victim thinking will lead you to forgo the wonderful experience of raising children, or it will increase the likelihood that your kids will fall victim to the horrors of incest. Mending your splits and shedding the victim role allows you to understand and accept the fact that you have control over your behavior. You have the power and the responsibility to raise children without subjecting them to sexual abuse. Incest is not a genetic, untreatable illness. Interrupting the incest cycle requires two things. First, you must truly want to stop this devastating pattern of behavior. Second, you must be willing to make the necessary changes for yourself in order to use your ability to end it. Unfortunately, many victims of incest become blocked when it comes to making changes because they don't know what changes to make, or they are too frightened to implement them.

12
Mending Our Splits

Becoming a safe, nurturing, and effective parent is an attainable goal, but this doesn't come about merely by wishing for it to happen. If we're truly committed to making life better for our children than it was for us, we must first learn to take good care of ourselves. We begin by identifying and repairing our own damage through accepting and then mending the mind/emotion/body/spiritual splits within ourselves. The little child within us must learn to bond and accept nurturing if we are to know how to bond with and nurture our own children. The little child within us must feel loveable and worthy if we are to communicate messages of self-love and self-worth to our own children. Parenting from an emotionally empty foundation risks sexual, physical, and emotional abuse. Emotionally empty parents increase the likelihood of role reversal, where they expect their children to parent them.

Relationship with Ourself

It's not easy to learn how to care for ourselves. Psychotherapy with an experienced, competent, and compassionate healer is a critical part of change. Reading self-help books, including those on effective parenting skills, also helps. Active participation in a Twelve Step support group (such as Adults Recovering from Incest, Incest Survivors Anonymous, Adult Children of Alcoholics, and Al-Anon) is a valuable way to examine issues and establish connections with people who understand our emotional pain and how to recover from it.

I must also warn you about support groups. They are dependent on the health of the individual members when it comes to healing. If you find yourself in a group which focuses only on superficial issues, or if the group is made up of people who abuse through shaming, look for another group. If you stay with a dysfunctional group you will only repeat your family of origin experience.

The time spent in support groups and therapy should feel supportive yet challenging. We should receive help identifying issues and hear healthy, corrective messages which aid our healing. If this isn't happening, we must grant ourselves permission to change therapists and/or support groups.

Effective psychotherapy must address all aspects of who we are if it is to help us. It may be very tempting to find a therapist who only operates from the head and doesn't challenge us to get into our feelings. This will only serve to maintain or even worsen the mind/emotion/body/spiritual splits within us. Similarly, a New Age healer who fails to understand that our spiritual being is grounded in a body of emotions will do little to assist with mending our splits.

Relationship with a Higher Power

Being victimized by incest may have led us to believe that we can't rely on sources outside ourselves for protection and nurturance. We may feel alienated from and embittered toward a Higher Power. After all, where was God when we needed Him most?

Comments like the following reflect a belief that we are doomed to live life without spiritual support: "Everyone else is worthy of God's love and help except me. God abandoned me because I'm no good." Too often, people behave as if there is a vindictive God who gave us all these desires and no way to fulfill them. We must find ways to change the victim thinking about our Higher Power. Healing the shame within us is a giant step toward mending our spiritual split and opening us up to nurturance and guidance from God. Spiritual integration empowers us with hope for change because all tasks become easier when we know we don't have to face them alone.

If we operate from the premise that God gave humankind both desires and the means to satisfy them, we can stay out of the victim role and avoid being dominated by victim thinking. A relationship with a Higher Power is a necessary first step toward following through on a commitment to ourselves to live healthy, functional lives.

13

Relationship with Family of Origin Members

Changing our relationships with family of origin members is generally some of the most painful and difficult work we do in our recovery. It entails tremendous grieving as we move toward acceptance and forgiveness, followed by redefinition and restructuring. Most incest survivors initially believe they have no choice when it comes to family relationships. The thinking usually goes something like this: family is family and this is a rule that must be accepted and not tampered with. Shedding the victim role as an adult, as well as protecting our children from the threat of abuse, requires that we challenge this unhealthy rule. We must assess family relationships and evaluate them based upon what feels honest, healthy, and right for us and for our children.

In addition to the incest perpetrator, you must make difficult decisions regarding your relationships with other family members. The critical issue is the extent to which other family members are capable of establishing and maintaining a respectful relationship with you. Do they choose to remain victims of the dysfunctional family system? Do they demonstrate a willingness to change existing patterns of thinking, feeling, and behaving?

A healthy relationship between two adults—whether family members, friends, or spouses—depends on a balance in the energy being committed by both parties. The giving and receiving which form the foundation of a relationship must roughly balance out over time, otherwise, the relationship is polluted by manipulation and victimization. For example, if you always call your parents to see how they're doing but they never call to ask about you, this relationship is out of balance and unhealthy. If your sister constantly gives you advice about your life but never requests your input about her, this relationship is out of balance and unhealthy. When such relationships are resistant to correction, think seriously about whether to continue them, and consider the impact of such a decision on your recovery.

Disclosing the Secret

For incest survivors in recovery, one of the best indicators of relationship balance is the degree to which family members share in the ownership of past mistakes and accept responsibility for the emotional pain inflicted. When we attempt to discuss with our parents and siblings what it was like to grow up in our family, including the horrible reality of incest, we will quickly find out whether anyone wants to heal the family.

Disclosing the secret of incest and opening up communication about family dysfunction begins to dismantle barriers which have separated us for many years. If our family members are willing to do the difficult and painful work required, this can mark the start of important and rewarding healing for everyone involved.

Some or all family members may refuse to face the incest, especially if the incest history is extensive and if alcoholism is present in the family. These members may be unable to do the work necessary for healing and resolution. Our parents may be a bit less stressed now that their children are grown and they may have mellowed somewhat with age, but the presence of an entrenched personality disorder or the power of denial and fear may preclude meaningful change. If family members are not open to change, we must accept this as we determine the best course of action for ourselves.

Must the Secret Be Disclosed?

Some people decide to not confront their parents about the incest because they believe their parents are not receptive to change. Although I respect the right of each of us to heal in our own manner, confrontation can be a powerful way to take back our power, perhaps for the first time, in these important relationships. We become stronger when we are open about our abuse in the presence of those who have abused us.

It's extremely important that you not confront your parents in order to receive validation that the incest really happened. Looking for admission and confession goes against the notion of owning your power as a way of breaking free from the victim role. Don't talk with your parents about the incest until you know in your heart and gut that it occurred. Talking with them is one way you can exercise your power to speak the truth—*whether or not they ever agree with or confirm your story*. Talking about the secret liberates you from the oppressive burden of protecting others through your silence. Not wanting to upset or hurt family members by speaking of the incest is a common but unhealthy reaction. It demonstrates inappropriate boundaries when you assume responsibility for others' feelings by shielding them from having to face emotional pain.

When you trust yourself enough to speak the truth, you are saying to yourself and to your abusers that the abuse is finally over. Although your words will be your own, this captures the essence of what is being communicated:

I know for myself what happened.
I can stand to have you angry with me
for speaking out. I can tolerate
not receiving your love and acceptance
if this is necessary.
I am not responsible for the incest;
you are. I am a worthy, good, and
whole person regardless of what you say.

During all my years of working with incest clients, I have only once strongly discouraged someone from confronting her abusive father. I took this unusual step because I considered him to be an extremely evil and dangerous man. This man had participated for many years in Satanic rituals involving violent behavior. There was no evidence indicating he had ceased doing this. Confronting him directly presented little opportunity for healing, but much risk for harm.

At first, most of us consider abusive parents too dangerous to confront, but in reality they rarely are. We project the terror we felt as helpless, powerless children into our present adult situation. One of the goals of psychotherapy is to help us understand that we are no longer victims and we are now able to protect ourselves from those who abused us in the past.

How Will Family Members React to the Disclosure?

The worst our abusive parent is likely to do is deny the truth in a loud, angry, and verbally abusive way. As adults, we can decide not to be contaminated by this behavior. We are free to leave if the behavior is objectionable. We can also decide who to have with us for protection when we do the confronting. We need not repeat our childhood experience of having to face this person without the aid of a protective adult. Most of my clients discovered their abuser is now a frightened, old person who appears empty, shallow, frail, and pathetic.

Reactions to disclosure of the secret follow a common pattern. One parent is shocked and the other denies the incest ever occurred. After a period of uncomfortable distancing, our parents make an effort to be close, loving, and giving without addressing the incest any further. This is their attempt to make up for the abuse without ever having to admit to it or talk about it. Everyone silently agrees to get on with life, knowing the truth but avoiding it.

Another common scenario is for the denial to be followed by strained distancing that never gets filled in. The relationship between parents and child either slowly fades to the point of minimal contact, or it eventually dies off entirely. It is very difficult to break the rule which states we must stick together as a family. Because of the shame and punishment handed out whenever this rule is challenged, many of us simply elect to put in as little time as possible with our parents and bide our time until they die.

Some incest survivors work very hard at blocking out and ignoring the negative aspects of their parents, while searching for the positive in them. They do this consciously and with the recognized goal of continuing to be a part of a family system. If the person is very skilled at the process of letting go, this strategy can occasionally produce a workable outcome. It is critical that expectations of what will be received in this context be realistic, otherwise it will only result in continued victimization and disappointment.

Perhaps the most powerful factor in a decision to stay with dysfunctional family relationships is the subconscious realization that leaving will trigger prolonged, painful, and intense grieving. The loss can feel overwhelming when we realize that our loving, healthy family of origin is only an illusion. This grief requires time to resolve and is very painful. Some people try to avoid all of it by playing a game with themselves and living out the illusion. Unfortunately, living a lie generates pain as well.

In some families or with some family members, losing you will be a very big deal. In other families or with certain family members, this loss may not be a big deal. A parent who has nothing to give generally feels burdened by an unwanted child regardless of the child's age.

If your parents are divorced, you may discover that one of them is more open to confronting the truth about the past. Often the decision to terminate a marriage means one partner in an unhealthy relationship has changed, and this person may now have the courage to implement other changes. If so, he or she may be available to really listen to you, and may offer some support as you move through recovery.

Sometimes we make the mistake of testing one family member to see if that person is open to change, and then assume all other family members will react the same way. This is victim thinking. You are also thinking like a victim if you decide you can't make changes because it would be an act of betrayal on your part.

Exercise your power and responsibility, as well as a basic sense of fairness, by testing all the relationships. Perhaps they will all turn out to be characterized by denial and abuse, but you may have the potentially healing experience of encountering a sibling who is capable of facing his or her pain and is willing to hear about yours. It would be such a waste to break contact with a brother or sister based on an erroneous assumption that all family members are alike.

Reversing the Power

Once you have forgiven acts of the past, you still must decide what you wish to establish for the future. The forgiveness process is so empowering for the victim because it doesn't require anything on the part of the abuser. It reverses the power relationship between victim and abuser by allowing the victim to finally be in control. You can use your understanding, growth, and perception to let go and move forward. Forgiveness helps you discard the victim role and become instead a survivor, as you actively choose to stop diverting so much energy into staying angry with the abuser.

Forgiveness doesn't necessarily mean moving from anger to embracing and loving the abuser. It might allow you to reach a point where you open your heart to him or her, or it might consist of simply finding a neutral, indifferent place with regard to this person. Any choice the abuser makes about a relationship with you in the present will likely have a profound impact upon which path you take. Of course, it is not only the incest perpetrator who must make these choices, but also others within the family. Are they willing to own appropriate responsibility for what happened? Are they open to put as much into a relationship with you as they take out? Do they show an active, sincere interest in you, including the problems and the pain, or are they only interested in focusing on themselves? Answers to questions such as these should serve to guide you in determining how to structure relationships with family members after you have forgiven them.

Remember, there is no universal right or wrong outcome to this process. What is right is simply to do what is most healing for you. Whether or not you have an ongoing relationship with all, some, or no members of your family of origin doesn't determine your worth and goodness as a human being. Your decisions are yours alone and are based on your own unique set of needs. The fact that a particular course of action might be appropriate for another person is irrelevant, because this other person isn't you. Trust and believe in yourself to find love, support, and happiness.

14

Relationship with Friends and Work

As incest survivors, we often do not believe we have a fundamental right to enjoy healthy, fulfilling relationships with others. This victim thinking frequently has its origin in dysfunctional relationships with schizoid, narcissistic, or psychopathic abusers. When you are still victimized by the old relationships, you surround yourself with people who take, abuse, and neglect. You give away power by only being involved with people who come to you. You are too shameful or too fearful to extend yourself by reaching out to people and drawing in those who desire to have healthy, balanced relationships.

Moving into new relationships as you grow is a natural part of recovery. This contradicts what you were taught as children, that loyalty to the family is valued above all else. The dysfunctional message is that relationships are forever, no matter how devastating the cost to the individual. It can be confusing when you are hanging in there with a friend "through thick and thin," because it isn't always clear whether this action reflects strength or entrapment. You will get better at making this distinction, sometimes following painful trial and error. Be gentle with and trust yourself while you develop skill at separating balanced friendships from emotionally abusive ones.

For a time, you might be feeling so much grief from other losses that you resist bringing anything else to an end. You may end up enduring neglect or abuse rather than initiating another loss. Of course, this loss would really be a gain since it would mean an end to the neglect or abuse, but understanding this cognitively might not do much in the short run to alleviate the pain.

Job Relationships

How many times have you said, "My boss is just like my father (mother). He (She) makes me feel like a stupid little kid." This suggests you are in a relationship just like the one with your parents. Your boss may have a helpless schizoid personality that you cover for and protect. Your boss may be a narcissist who doesn't really care about you and who drains you emotionally with self-centered preoccupation and a need for constant praise. A narcissistic boss will never really appreciate your extra effort and will take your long hours for granted. A psychopathic boss will treat you the same way, but will also expect you to take part in illegal acts. You will be expected to cover for your boss's embezzling, tax evasion, or whatever. I often hear about work settings in which there is a narcissistic male manager and a shaming, nonprotective female supervisor who pits her subordinates against each other while serving the narcissist's insatiable needs, much like the family dynamic many of us endured. When our workplace dysfunctions aren't open to repair, we may need to find a different job with healthier people as we go about our recovery.

Sexual Harassment

Male narcissists and psychopaths frequently

engage in sexual harassment of female subordinates. If you have learned that self-worth is defined through sex, you are an easy target for sexual harassment. You may even put out signals that invite this behavior as you seek personal validation. It's critical that you reject sexual demands from people who are using power to get what they want. This applies to sexual comments, sexual touch, or actual demands for sex. There are laws against sexual harassment and agencies to help protect you from this kind of abuse. You must not tolerate sexual victimization now that you are an adult. You have the power and responsibility to stop this behavior.

Overall Victim Thinking

You need to be careful about victim thinking in many areas at work. Putting in overtime without getting compensated when others either go home on time or get paid for their extra hours is an example of victim thinking on the job. Always working the holidays or taking the least desirable time for vacation to accommodate others reflects victim thinking. Tolerating being denied promo-

tions and raises on a regular basis can also sig-
nify victim thinking. Do you see yourself in
either of the following examples?

- It would be nice to have that holiday off this
  year, but I'm sure I'll have to work it, won't I?

- I know the budget probably can't handle me
  getting a raise, so I'm not really expecting one.
  Even though it would be nice to get one, I
  understand.

If victimization in the workplace is an issue for
you, watch how those you perceive to be nonvic-
tims assert themselves. Their actions will show
you how you might change your role. Although
you have to respect the hierarchy in a work situation, this doesn't mean you must subject yourself
to ongoing abuse. It's important to eliminate your
own part in initiating or perpetuating victimization on the job.

What We Can Get from Work

Work helps you recognize that you're intelli-
gent, competent, and capable. It allows you to feel

a part of something important and gives you a daily purpose in life. Usually you receive acceptance and appreciation for your productivity and performance. Work offers an opportunity to express your creativity. It is truly valuable if you understand what you can and can't get from it. Work can't become the family you missed and it can't fill in the gaps or meet the unfulfilled needs of your childhood. Knowing your needs and striving to meet them appropriately is a sign that your recovery is well under way.

15

Relationship with Spouse and Children

Assuming that your healthier part helped you choose your current spouse, you may still need to make some changes in this relationship. It may be that you need to bring the power base into balance and change how decisions are made. This change comes when you shed the victim role. Changes can be scary for both partners because the old stability within the marriage is disturbed. Ultimately, the whole family benefits because you increase your self-confidence and become more effective in role modeling for your children. And you or your spouse will no longer have to shoulder a disproportionate share of the responsibility within the family.

Many incest survivors remain in marriages with abusive spouses chosen for unconscious reasons through victim thinking. You may be married to someone who is very similar to your abusive parent. If so, you need to recognize this and decide what to do. This may require confronting the fact that you have taken on the same passive, helpless role modeled by your victim parent, and consequently have placed your children at risk.

If you married a schizoid, you are likely living a very confining, stifling life-style. You probably avoid taking the risk of expressing your creative energies and expanding your social network because you sense this is too threatening for your socially underdeveloped spouse. Breaking the incest cycle requires stretching yourself beyond an isolating, dependent marriage by establishing meaningful relationships with other people. Your children will benefit immensely if you take the lead in letting fresh air and bright light into your enmeshed family system.

If you married a narcissist, you are likely living a life characterized by extreme sacrifice and emotional self-deprivation. There is little opportunity for your self-esteem to flourish because all praise and credit must go toward maintaining your spouse's inflated ego. Your goals are ignored entirely, or at best addressed only after your spouse's. You silence yourself so as to avoid challenging your mate's insatiable thirst for power and control. Your children may be used as pawns to serve selfish desires.

If you are married to a psychopath, you are forever being conned. You and your children are at risk to be physically, sexually, and emotionally abused, and then told you are making a big deal out of nothing if you object. You repeatedly make excuses for him and cover up his illegal activities and con jobs. You look the other way when you sense extramarital affairs. When you allow your spouse to batter you because you have inadequate funds to leave him or because you are scared of your abuser, you are trapped by dangerous victim thinking. Many women reject available social service assistance for long-term help because they don't believe they can break free for good.

I don't want to minimize the fear many women have in abusive relationships. It is very real and well-founded. There are tragic true stories about women who leave their partners only to be tracked down and killed. It's important to remember, however, that these incidents, although horrifying, remain the exception and not the rule. We all feel fearful when we think about making changes, but we can't allow this fear to dominate and control our lives and keep us from moving forward. We must acknowledge the fear and take safety precautions in dealing with the frightening situation, but we must nevertheless do what we need to do to get away, and we must take our children with us.

If you elect to stay in a dysfunctional marriage, you must realize you are making a choice to do so. You shouldn't lie to yourself by saying you have no choice. You must know why you are staying and you must continue to work toward either improving the relationship or gradually developing the strength to leave. Lying to yourself models victimization to your children, perhaps in the same way one of your parents modeled it for you. It is your responsibility to interrupt and terminate the incest cycle.

Your Children

After reading this far, you probably have a better understanding of some of the mistakes your parents made while they were raising you. If you have children, you are likely in touch with your own parenting errors, some of which may be remarkably similar to those committed by your parents. By shamelessly and courageously confronting the truth about your own mistakes, you gain the knowledge and the strength to break the generational incest cycle. If you ignore the painful realization that abuse may have already victimized your children, your ignorance only serves to perpetuate the cycle.

If you have children, it is helpful to talk openly with them as you go through the process of healing and changing. When you explain that some of your parenting techniques aren't appropriate, that this isn't their fault, and that you are committed to making positive changes, you provide a validating experience for your children. Just think how helpful it has been if your parents owned their mistakes, or how healing it would feel if they did so. Simply talking about past mistakes isn't enough, though. Children get a sense of safety and a feeling of hope from seeing parents' behaviors change to match their words. Children resist change because of their natural fear of the unknown, but at the same time they welcome it if there is genuine potential for improvement. For example, if you resume your parenting responsibilities while insisting your children return to being kids, their initial resistance will be followed by relief after they truly believe the change is permanent.

Becoming a healthier and more competent parent requires filling in informational gaps. You must learn exactly what healthy parent-child relationships consist of, what developmental needs children have, and how you can most effectively satisfy these needs as a responsible parent. For example, children need both love and structure. But parents who were not taught how to nurture with appropriate boundaries find it very difficult to combine unconditional love with structure in a way that produces emotionally healthy, safe, and appropriately-behaved kids. If you have no information to help close this gap, you will tend to parent from one extreme or the other: either abusive, rigid discipline which produces unhappy, frightened children, or inadequate guidance and structure which leads to ungrateful, spoiled, and manipulative brats.

Looking for Trouble Spots

Preschool girls love to play at being a mommy and a wife. This behavior is developmentally appropriate. It's important for daughters to receive validation for their feelings without their mothers feeling threatened during this phase. What daughters need most is unconditional love with appropriate limit setting. They need to know that their mother likes seeing the closeness the daughter enjoys with her father, but the daughter also needs to hear that Daddy already has a wife. Daughters should not be allowed to take over mother's place within the home. Pretending to be married to Daddy is fine as long as it's clearly spelled out that it is pretending.

An insecure mother may become hurt and jealous in response to her daughter's behavior and consequently distance herself from both the child and her husband. The child should never be given the power to separate her parents, but it happens all too often. The risk is that with the woman being absent, a personality-disordered man might play into his child's fantasies and seduce her into being his emotional support, friend, and lover. This is not to say that the perpetrator isn't responsible for the incest; he most definitely is. What it does say is that you must guard against your own dysfunctional behavior in your role as parental protector if you are to successfully terminate the incest cycle. This incestuous dynamic happens in much the same way with preschool boys. With an absent father and a needy mother, the son gets taken seriously during his game of playing prince and is seduced by his mother in order to satisfy her sexual and emotional needs.

During adolescence children explore the world, gain independence, and discover their sexuality through accepting their bodies. Parental reactions and behaviors are very important in shaping self-concept and in learning how to establish and maintain appropriate boundaries during this crucial developmental stage. A healthy father senses the sexual energy in his daughter and doesn't allow it to blend with his own and stimulate him. He remains separate from her sexuality by containing his own. In other words, he doesn't play into her experimental flirting by pretending to be her boyfriend. His validation of her comes strictly from his role as a loving father.

A child isn't supposed to know how to contain her sexual energy at this age, but her father is. She should be able to learn sexual boundaries by observing them as demonstrated by her parents. She should never have to be burdened with feeling sexual energy from her father. If she does, covert incest, at the least, is taking place. It is the mother's job to watch for an unhealthy dynamic between daughter and husband and to step in and protect her if necessary. Similarly, boys should be able to rely on their fathers to step in if their mothers are sexually exploiting their developmental vulnerability.

Even when a marriage is not fulfilling, it is never acceptable for a child to fill in for an absent spouse. Many couples experience marital discord but manage to keep their children out of it. They avoid turning to their children for the solution. They work on their marriage, they separate or they divorce, but they never use their children as smoke screens for their problems, nor do they victimize them to satisfy adult needs.

Providing a Healthy Emotional Environment

It is the parents' job to provide a healthy emotional environment for their children. You must be careful not to unconsciously displace your anger or rage from the incest by directing these feelings at your spouse, kids, or pets. You must immediately stop perpetrating any physical or verbal abuse, put reasonable limits on your swearing, and cease breaking property when you want to release anger or rage. You can begin using some of the anger reduction techniques described in the previous chapters. You can teach your children how to release their anger so their bodies feel better and so they learn that it's not okay for them to act out their anger violently. This makes it much easier for everyone when you need to release anger. With an open but safe attitude about anger within the family, you can say to your kids, "Mommy is really mad right now so I'm going into my room and get rid of it. If you hear some noise you don't need to be worried or scared." You should reconnect with your children immediately thereafter, so they can see for themselves that everything is okay.

Infants, toddlers, and very small children will likely react to the loud sounds of released rage by experiencing shock, so I advise against releasing this intense anger where they can see or hear it. Screaming into a pillow muffles the sound and avoids distressing vulnerable children while still allowing you to discharge the feeling.

You can openly display to your children, along with a clear message that it isn't their job to "fix" this emotion. This teaches them that sadness is okay, and it demonstrates appropriate boundaries of responsibility for emotions. Kids also need to know that you get scared, but they shouldn't be burdened with the details of your fear. They should be reassured that you have resources to turn to in order to get beyond it. Never hold back joy. Provide your children with every available opportunity to connect with and express this exhilarating feeling.

You must help your children experience the world both through their minds and their bodies. Learning what their thoughts and feelings are all about helps them feel integrated within themselves. This helps them avoid or minimize the pain associated with mind/emotion/body/spiritual splits.

Setting Limits with Your Family of Origin

Incest has probably been part of your family history for generations. In order to stop the cycle, you must recognize that your children are also at risk for being emotionally and sexually abused by their cousins, aunts, uncles, grandparents, and even great-grandparents. It's your job to provide close supervision over what happens when your kids spend time with their relatives. Your children also need to hear loudly and clearly that you are open and available to hearing about any uncomfortable situations they encounter involving family members. In deciding what to do with your relationships with family of origin members, it's very important that you consider the effects of your decisions on your children. You may be able to tolerate a lot of abusive behavior just to be able to feel a part of a family unit, but what about your kids? They do not need to be part of an extended family if the price tag is risk of sexual and/or emotional abuse. They deserve better than to be exploited by dysfunctional relatives.

Protecting Your Children from Other Abusers

You will also need to watch over the dynamics of your children's relationships with baby-sitters, coaches, ministers, teachers, parents of friends, and others who might be serving in protector roles. Teach your children about what they do not have to put up with in relationships and be on the lookout for signs of unmet needs which are vulnerable to exploitation. If, for example, your daughter is placing too much emphasis on her sexual self, she may be trying to get validation of her self-worth through sex. This makes her particularly vulnerable to abuse from older men. Your task as a parent is to help her get the proper validation so she doesn't get used. Open communication is the most effective way to teach and validate your children.

Where to Turn for Answers

In addition to books and magazines which present useful information on parenting, many school systems, mental health agencies, and churches offer groups that teach parenting skills and simultaneously provide opportunities to share the joys, fears, and frustrations associated with parenting. Competent psychotherapists are generally knowledgeable about parenting techniques and the needs of children.

Along with information from external sources, you can turn to yourself for guidance as to what your kids need. You can look within yourself and ask what you were looking for at various ages when you were growing up. As you make progress in healing your spiritual split, you can access your spiritual being to know what constitutes positive parenting behavior. There are many sources of help open to you as you go about the process of stopping the incest cycle. You can't erase the past, but you can change the present and the future. You aren't a bad person if your children have been traumatized in the past. You are a good person who may have done a poor job of parenting because you were poorly parented. If you are prepared to work at eliminating the crippling effects of victim thinking, you can now protect your children and help them heal. The benefits that result from ending the incest cycle accrue to you, your children, and the children of future generations.

References

Bass, Ellen and Laura Davis. *The Courage to Heal: A Guide For Women Survivors of Child Sexual Abuse*. New York: Harper and Row, 1988.

Blaha, Dionne C. *The Singing Bird Will Come: Living with Love, Strength, and Joy*. Park Ridge, Illinois: Parkside Publishing, 1992.

Bronson, Catherine. *Growing Through The Pain: The Incest Survivor's Companion*. Park Ridge, Illinois: Parkside Publishing, 1989.

Butler, Pamela E. *Self Assertion for Women—New Edition*. San Francisco, California: Harper and Row, 1981.

Crook, William, M.D. *The Yeast Connection*. Jackson, Tennessee: Professional Books, 1983.

Eastman, Rebecca with Patricia Ryan. *Full Circle Fitness: Beyond Your Own Personal Trainer*. New York: William Morrow and Company, 1990.

Hay, Louise L. *You Can Heal Your Life*. Santa Monica, California: Hay House, Inc., 1984.

Keleman, Stanley. "Trust and Self-Reliance," Clinical Studies in Somatic Process, Professional Education Series. Berkeley, California: Center Press, 1980.

Krisch, Karl, M.D. Bioenergetics Training Session. Minneapolis, Minnesota: December 3 and 4, 1983.

Kushner, Harold S. *When Bad Things Happen to Good People*. New York: Avon Books, 1981.

Lowen, Alexander, M.D. *Bioenergetics*. New York: Penguin Books, 1975.

Lowen, Alexander, M.D. *Narcissism: Denial of the True Self*. New York: MacMillan Publishing Company, 1985.

Lowen, Alexander, M.D. *Pleasure: A Creative Approach to Life*. New York: Penguin Books, 1970.

Middleton-Moz, Jane. *Shame and Guilt.* Deerfield Beach, Florida: Health Communications, Inc., 1990.

Orbach, Susie. *Fat is a Feminist Issue.* New York: Berkley Books, 1978.

Peck, M. Scott. *The People of the Lie: The Hope for Healing Human Evil.* New York: Touchstone, Simon and Schuster, 1983.

Peck, M. Scott. *The Road Less Traveled.* New York: Touchstone, Simon and Schuster, 1978.

Richter, Betts and Alice Jacobsen. *Something Special Within.* Marina del Rey, California: DeVorss and Company, 1978.

Truss, C. Orian, M.D. *The Missing Diagnosis.* Birmingham, Alabama: 1982.